Eros

THE JOURNEY HOME

Reclaim Your Desires.
Awaken Your Feminine.
Trust the Erotic.

Megan D. Lambert

Authorsunite.com

*For all of our daughters, and especially for the daughter
who's growing inside me.*

PRAYER FOR THE BOOK

May this book activate a deep remembering in you.
May it call forth a part of you that is primal, instinctual, earthly and wise.
May you feel more whole, more accepted and more alive after going on this journey with me.

May this book go beyond you and me.
May the impact of Eros ripple through us and beyond us, touching each person we meet, changing lives just by living as desire-led women.
May the inner fire we stoke here spread like a blazing bonfire, lighting up women all over the world. Without even knowing why, the room gets a little brighter because we are in it.

May this work help our families, friends and communities draw closer together.
May we open our hearts more fully, allowing more love to be given and received.
May we feel the courage to be more honest, more ourselves in the world.

Lastly, may our children inherit a more beautiful, more true earth.
May our babies, and especially our daughters, feel more free, more unapologetic and more fully themselves than we ever could.

And so it is. Amen.

TABLE OF CONTENTS

WELCOME

*"There is no greater agony than bearing
an untold story inside of you."*

—Maya Angelou

We're in a time of massive feminine revival. Can you feel it? The tides are turning fast.

For thousands of years, women have been oppressed, degraded, disgraced.

Patriarchy, the cultural paradigm rampant in the US and Europe where I grew up, disconnects women from their inherent nature. Women are taught to be afraid of everything that makes them female—their menstrual blood, the power of pregnancy and birth, their sex, their heart's longings.

We've learned it is not powerful to be feminine. To succeed in a patriarchal world requires women to repress their feminine nature and to become more masculine—assertive, dominant, decisive and competitive. While possible, this causes great harm to our inner and outer world.

Disconnecting from our feminine (and trying to be only masculine) takes a toll on our bodies. Adrenal fatigue, breast cancer,

1

burnout and exhaustion are on the rise for a reason. Sometimes this disconnection is more subtle—felt as a vague dissatisfaction, as if something is missing.

The loss of connection to our feminine nature has stripped us of a vital aspect of being human, which is not just impacting women—it's impacting humanity as a whole.

The way we treat the earth reflects the (lack of) respect we have for the feminine—pillaging natural resources for personal gain, destroying centuries-old forests and hunting animals to extinction, to name a few. The ecology of the planet shows what happens when the masculine and the feminine are not in balance.

When our drive to conquer overpowers our instinct to cooperate. When the need to dominate replaces the call to collaborate. When the impulse to hunt is stronger than the impulse to nurture and sustain.

The earth's destruction is a wake-up call for how we treat the feminine.

We need both masculine and feminine energy—in balance. When we are out of balance like this, our bodies, our communities and our earth are ravaged.

The pain of the planet mirrors the pain of the repressed feminine.

It's time to wake up. NOW.
We don't have time to waste.
We matter to the ecology of our planet. We matter to our communities. We matter to ourselves.

When we work to reclaim our inner femimine, we naturally deepen our appreciation for the outer feminine—for the earth, for other humans, for a more sustainable way of living.
We become more generous, more aware, more heart-centered.
We trust our intuition and stop ignoring what's wrong.
We believe in the power of our desires and trust ourselves to create a more beautiful earth.

The work you do here ripples out. It's important.

I'm Speaking to You

I wrote this book with a special tenderness for the woman who has the creeping feeling of vague dissatisfaction.

This woman may be successful, with many friends and resources, and yet, she feels as if there's something more, as if she's not quite fully living. She's done everything she's "supposed to do," and yet...it doesn't fulfill her soul's deepest longing. She may feel utterly alone in this sensation, as the people around her appear happy with life as it is.

Yet, she is not happy. She can feel she's not quite living a life of her own choosing, that she's following the script of other people's expectations. She longs to understand why the things that used to satisfy her no longer do, why she feels restless, unfulfilled.

Everywhere, I see women who don't know what they actually want. Women who feel disconnected from their bodies, their calling, their sex. Women who second guess their intuition and try to analyze their way through life, only to wonder why they're paralyzed by self-doubt. Women who are self-sufficient, self-reliant and strong... but secretly struggle with loneliness and ache for deep love.

While she may not yet have words for this restlessness, she can feel the edges of her wildish nature calling to her, beckoning her home, back to her intuition, to her desire and her sex.

Is this woman you?

This book can be your roadmap home—to finding your wild, sexy, feminine self. You'll discover a deeply nourishing place within yourself where you can rest, receive and dream. In short, you'll connect with Eros, the vibrant feminine soul.

Eros: A Remembering

When I graduated from my life coaching program many years ago, I was given a copper necklace that read: *Remember to Remember*. At first, I didn't understand the message, but over time this phrase has become one of my guiding principles.

Eros is remembering our ancient, primal wisdom which lies rooted in our erotic, intuitive impulses. Eros is the creative, sexy human animal, a raw vitality that moves through us, that speaks through us. Desire is the voice of Eros, the unique expression of our soul.

Connecting with Eros is coming home—to your feminine, to your wholeness, to your erotic, to all the parts of you that you were taught to hate, dismiss and ignore. As you find Eros, you'll remember your brilliance and your power.

My hope is that during this journey, you will glimpse the wild, powerful feminine part of you. Then you will forget her again.
The key? Remember to remember. Over and over.

I'm with you.
I believe in you.
Let's do this.

Sections of the Book

Remembering Eros is an ongoing, life-long process. The journey is more of an upward cycle than a linear process, though this book is laid out with a clear roadmap to follow.

This book is divided into four sections:

Emptying
Reclaiming
Opening
Sustaining

The first section is **EMPTYING.**

Before we can learn any new perspectives or skills, we have to let go of the old conditioning, the old stories, the old limitations and beliefs. We have to empty out.

Here we examine: What exactly is *cultural conditioning* and how do we let go of it? What do we need to forgive ourselves and others for? What has society told us that is not ours to carry anymore? This helps us feel **free**.

The next section is **RECLAIMING.**

Once we've created fresh inner-space through emptying out, we can reclaim the parts of us we may have neglected—our turn on, our pussy, our desire, our pleasure, our cycles, our emotions.

The section helps us integrate the darker, more "messy," more feminine aspects of ourselves that we may have undervalued or discounted until now. This helps us feel **whole**.

The third section is **OPENING.**

Now that we feel whole, we are ready to connect more deeply with others. This is where we explore sex, relating, interpersonal dynamics and love. We undertake the courageous journey of moving from self-reliance to interdependence. This helps us feel more **love**.

The last section is **SUSTAINING.**

By this point, you've likely felt a profound shift in your life. You're a different woman than you were when you began this journey. But how do you sustain this? What can you do to continue growing as an erotically alive, passionate, desire-led woman?

This section connects you with your deepest *why* to guide your life, and encourages you to build a community of women to support you. This helps you feel your **power**.

How to Use this Book

This book can change your life—if you let it. If you read the stories with your whole heart and do the exercises with intention, you will be on your way to a total mind and body transformation. You will feel more free, more whole, more love and more power than ever before.

How to get there?

Read one chapter at a time, and take time to integrate the information with the exercises. You can afford to go slowly here. This is deep, soul-altering work.

Make sure to do all the exercises, because that's where the information moves from intellectual theory into felt, embodied wisdom where Eros lives.

If you appreciate more specific guidance, here's my recommendation: set aside fifteen minutes a day to read and do one exercise. That adds up to roughly one and a half hours a week, which is usually manageable, yet powerful.

The information in this book may not be new to you, but it's your integration of the information—and your commitment to doing the exercises—that make this book life-changing.

Are you looking for an even more powerful way to experience Eros? Do this journey with a group of three-to-six friends. You can read a chapter a week together, sharing in the exercises and questions on which to reflect. This will give you community and support as you try on new behaviors and perspectives.

To help you personalize and deepen the content, I've created a guide for you to use while you read this book. This free guide helps you reflect and apply the learnings from each chapter for a more transformative experience. Download the guide here: **www.megandlambert.com/book**.

Buckle Up for Safety: Preparing for the Journey

On Mental Health
The tools and perspectives in this book are no substitute for mental health professionals. If you're struggling with mental health issues, please seek out professional advice.

These topics may bring up intense emotions. If you're feeling triggered by the content shared, please slow down, breathe deeply and get any support you need.

On Sexual Trauma
Sexual trauma is heartbreakingly common. In the US, one out of every six women has been the victim of an attempted or completed rape in her lifetime (statistics from RAINN).

This book is based on my personal story. Some of the stories may be intense to read, and in those cases, I have added a trigger warning beforehand so you can decide if you'd like to read those stories. While I do my best to be sensitive to trauma throughout the book, it does not specialize in sexual trauma or abuse. If you need specific resources around trauma or abuse, please seek them out.

On Gender
I am a cis-woman, with a pussy/vulva and a menstrual cycle. I identify as heterosexual and primarily talk about relating to men monogamously. My lens on sexuality and love is shaped by my identity, though I aim to be inclusive of all women—trans-women, those without a pussy/vulva, and different sexual orientations and agreements.

The concepts I share can be applied to many different love and sexuality situations. Please mentally substitute the gender pronouns and words you prefer to use. As always, take what you like and leave the rest.

On Privilege
Please know when I talk about "our culture," I am speaking from my own experience as a white, heterosexual USA citizen. I speak from a certain place of unearned privilege, having not experienced the same personal or cultural trauma millions of people have. I hope you find commonalities in what I share, while of course, I expect your story to be uniquely yours.

On Lineage
In sharing perspectives and tools from other cultures, I do my best to be respectful of the lineages and use this wisdom with full integrity. I thank you in advance for your forgiveness if I unintentionally misrepresent others' experiences and cultures.

On Client Stories
Throughout the book I use client stories to illustrate key points. All client names and identifying details have been changed to protect their anonymity.

On Being Triggered
You may feel upset or triggered while reading this book. The topics we cover are taboo, treacherous and emotionally charged. I don't know what may upset you, as each person is unique, so please do take good care of yourself while undergoing this journey.

On a more subtle level, you may encounter internal resistance to doing this work. For example, you may suddenly feel "too busy" for the exercises or abandon the book halfway through. This tends to happen when our previous way of living is being challenged. If you notice resistance, congratulate your self-awareness and then, if you can, keep leaning in, slowly and gently.

Emptying

"I could have spent the rest of my life trying to prove that I was a good girl—but that would have been unfaithful to who I really was. I believed that I was a good person, if not a good girl. But my appetites were what they were. So I gave up on the idea of denying myself what I truly wanted. Then I sought ways to delight myself ...

Anyway, at some point in a woman's life, she just gets tired of being ashamed all the time.
After that, she is free to become whoever she truly is."

—Elizabeth Gilbert in the novel *City of Girls*

CHAPTER 1

FORGIVING OURSELVES
AND OTHERS

Let's start with the last place you probably want to go—*forgiveness*.

Why start with forgiveness? Because together, we're about to undertake a powerful, life-changing journey. This journey will be much more challenging if we're carrying resentment and regret.

Regret, resentment, blame and shame are heavy burdens to carry. They make us feel tired, avoidant, discouraged. To move forward, we have to let go of what we've done—and what's been done to us. This process will feel as if we're cleaning out the closet of anything old, musty and no longer needed.

Forgiveness helps us understand the past and learn from it, maybe even appreciate it. In the process, we clear the slate regarding all those voices of what we could have, should have, would have done. We let it go. We let ourselves—and others—off the hook.

Specifically, when it comes to reclaiming our eroticism, we may have a lot of healing to do.

What and/or whom do we need to forgive? A few possible examples:

- our parents for only talking about the dangers, not the pleasures, of sex

- our friends for shaming us or judging our behaviors
- our culture for simultaneously objectifying and shaming women's sexuality
- our partners for forcing us to have sex before we're ready
- ourselves for making decisions that may not have felt good

I'm not going to say you need to forgive the people who hurt you. You get to choose that. Forgiveness can be a long journey you may or may not want to take. That's okay. Be patient with yourself.

Reading through this chapter will give you tools and perspective when you are ready to forgive. This process works, and it will be so, so worth it once you finish. The women who have gone through this process with me have had profound results. They feel clear. They feel lighter. They feel more self-compassion. You can, too.

As always, if you're working through a particularly traumatic experience, I recommend enlisting a professional to help.

First, let me share one of my darker stories and how I've found forgiveness there.

Trigger warning: *The story below contains sexual assault. Read with care.*

A Messy Night in Monaco

I am nineteen, visiting my parents in France for the summer. They want me to have fun, so they suggest I go out with their friends' son. He is eight years older than I and can show me around town. I agree.

He takes me to a fancy club in Monaco, where we buy shots and drinks. I feel tipsy and excited to be out in such an adult place, so I let him kiss me. The last thing I remember is kissing him at the bar.

Then I black out.

When I come to, he is already inside me.

He is on top of me, with my face down on a bed, my dress pulled up around my waist. Having awoken, I quickly shove him off of me, yelling, "What the f*ck are you doing?!" I'm horrified to discover he isn't wearing a condom—something to which I would have never, ever consented.

I pull down my dress and run out of his apartment, catching a cab on the street.

Once home, I stumble into bed and fall back asleep.

When I wake up, it all feels like a bad dream. My body is achy and sore, I feel nauseated, and my pussy hurts. I feel so ashamed and so afraid. How had this happened? What do I do now?

I knew I had to handle my health first and get a morning after pill, as I didn't know exactly what happened. I look up the French word for Plan B, make an excuse to my mom for leaving the house, and sneak out to the pharmacy, where I desperately try to explain what I want to buy.

The pharmacists look at me, hungover and ragged, with raised eyebrows and judgmental eyes. They whisper amongst themselves in French before eventually handing me a little white box. My cheeks burn hot—I want to die right there. I feel like a dirty slut.

I was too scared to tell anyone about that night. Not my mom, not my friends, no one. I kept that secret to myself for years.

I felt confused and ashamed.
Was I drugged, or did I drink so much I blacked out?
What had even happened?
How did I end up in his apartment?
Why do I not remember anything?
Was I passed out when he'd started having sex with me?

That thought made me feel sick to my stomach. Who does that? I was so angry with him, but more than anything, I was angry with myself. I was mad that I'd let myself get into an unsafe situation.

I argued I wasn't the kind of woman who did this. Before then, I had only had sex with a couple of long-term boyfriends I loved. I felt as if I had lost my innocence in this experience.

The Healing

I kept that secret to myself for a few years. When I was twenty-two, I volunteered with WYSE, an amazing organization called Women and Youth Supporting Each Other, where I mentored young girls from Compton, Los Angeles. One of the topics was sexual assault.

As I taught the young girls about how to prevent unwanted sexual experiences, memories of my own experience flooded back. I began to realize I didn't need to blame myself for what had happened—that painful experience didn't mean anything about me as a person.

I heard other women share their stories, many of which sounded just like mine. That gave me courage. I was not alone.

One day, I shared my story with a few friends, who listened kindly without judgment. Seeing the way my friends looked at me, not as a dirty whore but as a whole woman with a painful memory, healed something inside of me. They held me as I cried and cried. I felt years of shame and self-judgment leaving my body in their presence.

It also helped me to take action. By teaching about consent and even leading an initiative against sexaul assault in my university, I felt empowered. I didn't want experiences like this to happen to women ever again, and I wasn't helpless—I could do something to prevent it.

The Road to Forgiveness

Together, these steps showed me how I can forgive:

Hearing others' stories.
Sharing my own.
Feeling my feelings.
Remembering I'd done the best I could.
Taking a stand against wrongdoings.

It's not a linear journey to forgive, but it is entirely possible, for me and for you.

Forgiveness is never easy. It requires facing the pain of experiences many of us would rather leave as skeletons in the closet. But those skeletons haunt us and make us feel small and afraid. By facing these dark memories, we can begin to heal, to forgive, and eventually, to move forward.

Forgiveness Requires Feeling

There are moments, like mine above, that haunt us.

We may feel angry at the other person, resentful that they didn't behave better.
We may feel angry at ourselves, ashamed that we didn't have the courage to speak up or show up in a different way.
We may feel angry at life for bringing us such pain and heartache.
Or perhaps, we feel closed off, numb and afraid.

The healing comes when we're ready to feel below our numbness into the molten core of anger or the deep waters of grief and completely move through the emotions. This book, and especially Chapter 9, will help you feel your feelings.

> *There is no person alive who has not been hurt.*
> *There is no person alive who has not hurt others.*

There is no person alive who has not been hurt.
There is no person alive who has not hurt others.

That is an inescapable fact of living life, in these human bodies, on this planet.

The question is—what will we do with that hurt and that anger? Will we feel it and release it? Will we eventually maybe alchemize it into gratitude?

We Hurt Because We Were Hurt

Humans are not born as bad people who do evil things. We lash out or act out when we feel insecure, betrayed, angry or in pain. When we are trying to forgive ourselves, it helps to remember that our destructive behavior and patterns are learned.

Collectively, the world holds much pain and trauma. If you are "doing the work," it starts with clearing your piece of our collective pain, so you can live more freely, and in doing so, be an example to others.

Working on forgiving yourself reminds you that you don't have to be perfect to be loved.
You may have hurt people and still be loved. You may have caused harm, broken hearts, destroyed relationships—and still, you're lovable.

It can be exceptionally hard to forgive ourselves, especially for women. In general, men tend to blame others and hold onto resentments, while women often blame themselves and hold onto shame. So for many of the women I work with, hostility and anger toward themselves is usually the most difficult to heal.

We know we have caused harm. For example:

- We've said yes to a date with someone we weren't into and hurt their heart.

- We endured an abusive relationship for far too long.
- We've broken hearts.
- We had sex we didn't want to and blamed our partners.
- We've yelled cruel words at people we love.

We think if we carry around the shame of what we've done, somehow that shame will make us into better people.

Yet, shame begets shame. Shame disconnects us from ourselves and from others. When we're ashamed of what we've done, we'll continue to repeat those patterns and cause more harm.

It's time to release your shame and give yourself a little breathing room.

What to Forgive?

As you read this chapter, you may immediately know where you're still holding resentment toward others or shame toward yourself. Or it may be difficult to remember a specific moment.

If you're unsure who to forgive or for what to forgive yourself, start with a memory that makes you cringe. Moments you'd rather not share with others. Secrets you carry. Any people you feel particularly hardhearted, fearful or defensive around. These are often great indicators that you're holding a grudge—toward yourself or others.

Choose one memory or person to use through the rest of this chapter. You can come back to this process and these tools with each situation or person you want to forgive.

How to Forgive

Forgiveness can be a long journey. It does not need to happen overnight.
Or sometimes, forgiveness can happen suddenly and surprisingly.

Either way, it begins with willingness. Are you willing to acknowledge past hurts and then let them go?

In my personal experience, I learned how powerful these actions are in working on forgiveness:

- Hearing others' stories
- Sharing my own
- Feeling my feelings
- Remembering I did the best I could
- Taking a stand against wrongdoings

In the below meditation, I guide you through feeling your feelings (in a manageable way) and remembering you did the best you could. This can be a powerful experience.

Meditation: Forgiveness

Background

The meditation will help you forgive yourself and heal so you can move forward. I will focus specifically on challenging moments in your love and sex life, though feel free to broaden to other topics if more relevant for you.

Remember earlier when I asked you to recall a specific memory or person to forgive? Bring that memory or person to mind for this meditation. The following instructions will help you uncover what happened, why it happened and how to let it go. This meditation has helped many women I work with feel lighter and freer.

This meditation may be emotional. Welcome your tears or any emotions which arise. Tears are cleansing and are our body's natural way of allowing us to release stuck emotions.

If the emotions feel too intense for you, imagine a volume knob. Dial your emotions back to 20% or stop the meditation entirely. Keep this process manageable and be gentle with yourself.

I recommend reading through the meditation instructions completely a few times, then closing your eyes and guiding yourself through it. You can also find a free audio version on my website: **www.megandlambert.com/book**.

Instructions

Start by finding a comfortable place where you won't be disturbed.

Sit and close your eyes.

Feel your breath moving in and out of your body.

With each exhale, let your body soften.

Bring your attention to your body.

What areas feel tight?

What areas feel soft and relaxed?

Nothing to change or fix in your body, just notice.

Continue breathing deeply.

As you continue being aware of your breath and the sensations of your body, allow images of your past love or sex life to flash across your mind's eye, almost like watching a movie. You might picture ex-partners, dates you went on, sexual experiences you had.

Continue breathing as you see these memories appearing in your mind.

Then, choose one memory that feels painful or unhealed. This may be a memory where you feel ashamed, angry, resentful or afraid.

Continuing breathing deeply, feeling the ground beneath you and the surface on which you're sitting.

Notice your breath moving in and out.

Now, watch this painful memory in your mind's eyes, remembering you're the one watching it, like someone in the audience at a movie theater.

As you mentally review this memory, you may notice emotions start to well up. Welcome them warmly. Continue breathing.

If you begin to feel tightness in your body, especially your chest, your shoulders or your belly, acknowledge that tightness and welcome it, as well. Become aware of how this tightness is trying to protect you.

Now, see your part in the movie of this memory, almost as if you're zooming in on one of the actors. Notice:

- What are you doing in this painful memory from your past?
- What are you saying?
- What are you thinking?
- How are you behaving?

You might ask yourself, is there anything you wish you'd done differently?

Continue watching this memory with lovingkindness.

Notice any particular moments where you:

- Betrayed yourself

- Acted okay with something you weren't
- Didn't speak up
- Said yes when you meant no
- Lashed out from a place of pain
- Closed down your heart

As you recall this moment, notice if any part of your body tightens in response to it. Maybe your chest, your neck or your belly. If so, bring a hand to that part of your body— slowly, gently. As you feel the warmth of your hand on that part of your body, imagine sending yourself love and compassion.

Remind yourself whatever you did was because of something you experienced. We hurt because we were hurt. A little part of you faced a challenge, got overwhelmed and didn't yet have the necessary coping skills.

Continue to breathe into the kindness of that truth.

Imagine turning toward that part of you that got overwhelmed, that lashed out, or closed down, or lied, or whatever the behavior was.

Imagine that part of you is like a little child, maybe only three or four years old. Picture a small child doing that action. Can you have compassion for that small child part of you?

With each breath in, bring a little space into tight spots in your body, and with each breath out, let go more fully.

Forgiveness is a beautiful gift to give yourself. You deserve that gift.

Imagine that painful memory as a tight knot in your body. With each breath, imagine allowing that tight knot to soften, to melt.

Remind yourself that you're different now. You have evolved and changed. You may do the same behavior in the future, but this time with a different level of awareness and compassion.

Forgive yourself and continue to breathe deeply.

Now, I want you to see all of the good that has come since that "bad thing" happened.

Maybe you cheated on your husband, but you finally feel free of a marriage that didn't fit either of you.
Maybe you lashed out at a partner, but it opened up some honest truth.
Maybe you had sex you didn't want to have, but in the pain of that experience, you discovered more fully your body's "yes" and your "no."

What good has come from this "bad thing?"
How was this moment entirely necessary for your evolution?

When we weave these painful moments or "bad behaviors" into the tapestry of our lives, we can see the whole picture. We become whole humans, no longer having to reject a part of our history or a part of ourselves. We can walk away with the memory woven into the tapestry of who we are and who we are becoming.

Take another deep breath and let it out with a gentle sigh.

Come back to your room, your space, your feet on the ground, your hips in the chair.
Notice your breath moving in and out.

Today, you're starting a new chapter.
You're making new decisions.
You are a new woman with a new future.

Because of the way that you have forgiven and integrated in your past, you don't have to unconsciously repeat it. You've released a heavy weight and can now move more freely in the world.

Take one more deep breath in and out. With that, go about your day as the new woman you are, making new decisions, celebrating yourself with newfound compassion, generosity and kindness toward yourself and others.

Repeat this practice daily for a couple of weeks or until the major painful moments from your past feel softened and released.

Invitation: Grab Your Journal

1. What is **one** painful memory that lives in your past erotic or love life experiences?

2. What did you do that you'd like to avoid repeating?

    a. Examples: not holding your boundaries, being afraid to speak your needs, judging yourself, criticizing a loved one, etc.

    b. Focus only on YOUR behaviors. Be specific.

3. How do you feel about what happened?

    a. Allow yourself to feel any feelings that arise.

    b. Tears, anger and grief are all welcome as you do this journaling practice.

4. Can you forgive yourself, knowing you did the best you could?

    a. Bring a hand to your heart. Send yourself love and compassion.

    b. Remember, what you did came from an experience you had—it wasn't for no reason. A tender part of you faced a challenge she couldn't handle and used a coping mechanism. Can you have compassion for that tender part of you?

    c. When you forgive, you acknowledge that you did your best. You acknowledge you are learning, and you don't need to be perfect to be loved.

5. How did this "bad behavior" or painful moment create goodness in your life? How was this moment vital to the story of who you are today?

    a. When we integrate our painful moments, our mess becomes our message. We create meaning out of struggle.

Exercise: Share Your Shame

The most powerful way to clear shame is to share your story with another (loving, non-judgmental) person. I found so much freedom when I shared my "messy night in Monaco" story with friends. Seeing the love on their faces began to lessen my shame.

This exercise is an invitation to be vulnerable and to heal in connection. It can be a tender, life-changing experience.

Here's what I recommend:

1. Focus on one memory that feels particularly painful or stuck to you, yet which is also manageable to share with someone.

2. Choose a person with whom to share this memory. Consider:

   a. Has this person been gentle with your vulnerability in the past?

   b. Are they kind and compassionate with themselves? (If yes, it's likely they will be with you, too.)

   c. Do they feel trustworthy to you?

3. Ask this person if they'd listen to you share for ten to fifteen minutes about something that's been on your mind. Ask if they would be supportive and gentle with you without giving advice or trying to fix anything.

4. Set up a time and place for the conversation. Some ideas: on the phone, in the car, on a walk or sitting together having tea.

5. Once ready, share your story. Open up about not just what happened, but also how you felt in that moment. Share any stories you've made up about yourself as a result of what happened. Let yourself feel any feelings that arise.

6. After sharing, look at the other person. See the compassion and love in their eyes. Let yourself receive whatever support they offer.

7. Notice how you feel afterward. Freer? Lighter? Embarrassed? It's all welcome. Sometimes this process may bring up intense emotions or feel very uncomfortable. That's okay. It's part of the healing process.

CHAPTER 2

LETTING GO OF THE ACCOMMODATING "GOOD GIRL"

In the previous chapter, we cleared out space through forgiveness. Now it's time to ask ourselves—what am I doing or saying that is not true to me? Where in my life have I been conditioned to "please" rather than be authentic to myself?

If you are going to be a sovereign woman whose intuition and desires guide her life, the first step is to realize when you are NOT that. In other words, to see the places where you are trying to meet someone else's expectations rather than listen to your own inner voice.

We all do this.

As young girls, many of us were raised to be "sugar, spice and everything nice." When you're a fiery, passionate, emotional, creative, wild young girl, how do you become "everything nice?" You must deny yourself.

Many of us are conditioned from the time we're little to make other people comfortable (even if it hurts us), to say the right thing (even if it's fake), and to accommodate others' needs above our own (even if it makes us miserable).

This chapter is about understanding this cultural conditioning so we can become aware of it and let it go in order to reveal our body's innate wisdom.

The Accommodating Good Girl Snaps

By now, I have graduated university, and am dating a boyfriend named Daniel who seems so captivating and charming. He has grand visions for his life, and is always talking about the businesses he is going to start. Someday.

Unfortunately, that "someday" seems far from today. My phone rings and I look at the name —Daniel. "Ugh." I sigh inwardly. I know what my boyfriend wants to talk about. He is calling me to complain about his job at a tech firm. Again.

For the past nine months, at least once a week, he calls to tell me how much he hates his job. He rants about how stupid everyone else is (besides him), and how his entrenepreneurial talent is wasted at this big company. Every week, he vows to leave soon to start his own business.

Week after week, I've nodded dutifully and responded automatically. "Yes, you're right. That sounds terrible." He has a fiery temper, so I try not to say anything that may ruffle his feathers. I walk on eggshells around him. "Just listen and be supportive," I coach myself.

Until one day, I can't anymore.

I see his name on my phone screen and my body tightens. I answer the phone and he launches into a tirade about his work. This time, I snap, my blood boiling. With clenched teeth, I tell him, "You need to call someone else with this." Then I quickly hang up before my rage escapes my lips.

I'm absolutely furious. For months, I've listened to him complain about his job without taking action. For the first month, I was genuinely sympathetic, because I could see he was miserable. After that, I had to bite down and deny how annoyed I was in order to be the "accommodating good girlfriend."

At some point, the fuse had to break.

I grit my teeth and hang up the phone. I feel the anger inside me corroding my insides with acid. I have no idea what to do with so much pent up, unexpressed anger.

"Do I even respect this man?" I asked myself. This man who seemed incapable of living his own truth? My heart was closing to him. Shortly after, I broke up with him.

That unexpressed emotion ate me on the inside. I tried to be a "good" girlfriend by repressing the rage I felt—yet that repression prevented the deep, raw intimacy I craved. I justified it by saying I'm not sure he could handle my anger, but really, I doubted if I would be lovable if I let out my rage.

Unexpressed rage does not go away

This is a common pattern with the women I coach. They will deny their anger for months until they can't hold it in anymore. Then either their anger explodes outward as a fight, or the anger explodes inward and they get sick from all the stuck emotions.

It doesn't have to be like this.

Over the five or so years following this moment, I began deliberately working on listening to my body's signals when something felt frustrating. By tuning in more closely to my body and my emotions, I now understand my genuine *yeses* and *nos* more clearly.

From there, I worked on setting smaller boundaries, such as saying, "I'm unavailable today," rather than a big break-up-worthy outburst like in the above story. I hear my body's *no* quicker now and work to express it sooner. This helps me prevent the massive outbursts I used to have.

The People Pleaser Says Yes—Again

Following this breakup, I moved to a new city, where I was eager to make friends.

I attended a networking event at a local co-working space, where I talked to an older man. He said, "Do you want to go to a dance with me? That's where all of the locals are."

I said, "I'd love to." Even though I didn't know him at all, I loved to dance, so I was in.

He gestured for me to jump on his motorbike. I noticed he only had one helmet, which he did not offer to me.

I felt my body tighten. I never rode on bikes without helmets, but I didn't want to make a big deal out of it or appear overly dramatic.

So I got on the bike without a helmet, without saying a word.

He started driving fast, which scared me. I asked, "Please, can you slow down?"

He sighed and said, "Fine." A few minutes later, he started driving fast and I politely asked, "Please, can you slow down?"

Then he said the clincher line. "Gosh, don't you teach feminine empowerment work? You should know how to surrender."

I was so angry.

But again, to be polite, I closed my mouth and didn't say a thing. Then it started to rain. He had just one poncho, which he put on himself. *Seriously?!* I thought. *What a jerk!* I made a frustrated sound but said nothing. I was wet, soggy and fuming.

I stayed silent the rest of the drive. When we got to the dance, I walked away from him for good.

In all of these little moments, my body was telling me, "No, don't do this. This doesn't feel good." And yet, like many women, my cultural conditioning is to be nice, polite and easygoing. I didn't want to appear "dramatic," "crazy," or "demanding," so I went with the situation, even though it felt terrible.

How many times have you done that?

It is so, so common.

As little girls, we're expected not to demand too much, to be "easy" and "chill." This leads to a lot of grown women who deny their bodies' *yes* vs. *no* and then find themselves in unsafe or unpleasant situations.

However, each of these moments taught me something. I started noticing when something felt "off" and discovered what happens when I denied my own intuition. Conversely, I learned what happens when I trust my intuition, even if I don't understand exactly why.

The Mysterious Yeast Infections

I once coached a woman who was struggling to have sex with her husband. She didn't really want to be intimate with him, but she would allow it since he wanted sex so often. After the sex, however, she kept getting yeast infections.

She was working on the medical side of her yeast infections with her doctor but wondered if there might be an emotional component, as well.

Through my coaching clients, I've often noticed that yeast and bacterial infections occur when a woman's body is a *no* to something that's happening. It's as if her pussy is hoping she will hold her own boundaries, but if the woman doesn't, then her pussy has to hold the boundary for her via yeast infections or other

31

imbalances. *(By the way, curious why I use the word "pussy?" You'll find out in Chapter 5.)*

Over the course of a few weeks, we talked about how she could slow down, take her time and listen to her body. I reminded her that she never has to do anything sexually that she doesn't want. She began saying *no* to her husband, and let him deal with his own sexual frustration.

As it turned out, the messages her body was sending were much bigger than sex. A few months later, she found out her husband was cheating on her.

She had felt something was off about their relationship for at least a year and a half—and her pussy showed that "off-ness" with physical symptoms. But she didn't have the courage to listen, or to leave, until he cheated. Then she realized it was time to change.

The Body's Intuitive Nature

As Shakira sings, "My hips don't lie." Well actually, our whole body doesn't lie. Our bodies reveal the truth our minds may not want to acknowledge.

Why don't we want to acknowledge these truths? Well ...

Women grow up with messages including...

- Make people comfortable (even if you have to contort yourself).
- Follow the leader (even if you know better).
- Be happy and smile (even if you feel bad inside).
- Make reasonable decisions (even if your intuition feels beyond reason).

In short, the message is to *be an accommodating good girl*. Yikes! It's no wonder so many women struggle to hear the quiet whisper of their inner voice, why so many women second-guess themselves, doubt their decisions and hesitate to act.

Without the clear guidance of their body's intuition, women are left trying to navigate life without their inner compasses. Without our intuition, we are lost in a patriarchal world that doesn't have our best interests in mind.

But here's the truth: *our bodies never lie*. Every moment, our bodies are either opening or closing. Opening (expressing our "yes") feels warm, soft, relaxed. Closing (expressing our "no") feels tense, tight, cold.

We often move too fast and think too much to actually hear our bodies opening and closing.

- Our minds can easily bulldoze over the subtle whisperings of our body.
- Our minds can rationalize over the top of our intuition, which often feels quite primal, non-linear and non-logical.
- Our cultural conditioning kicks in, reminding us not to be "hysterical" or "dramatic," so we try to be chill (and ignore our deeper knowing).

This chapter will help you reprogram that cultural conditioning so you can hear the subtle whisperings of your body. In doing so, you will discover your deeper intuition, which will give you a map to making better decisions. No more second-guessing yourself!

Our Bodies Are Always Communicating

Our bodies talk. And we're really good at ignoring them.
But sometimes our bodies' signals become so loud we can't ignore them anymore.

There's a well-known metaphor called the *Feather, Brick, Truck*. It basically says that the Universe (or your body) speaks to you the first time as a feather-light whisper, a caress, a subtle gut instinct.

The second time the universe speaks by throwing a brick at you. The last time, it runs you over by a truck. That is how our soul communicates—in progressively louder volumes. We can choose at what volume we decide to listen.

Let's go back to the woman who was in the struggling marriage. The first whisper that her marriage was in trouble was the recurring yeast infection. The brick was her nagging feeling that something wasn't quite right. But she was so attached to her fantasy of their future together that she wouldn't admit what her intuition was telling her. Then the universe sent the truck—him cheating on her. The truth was there all along—this relationship was struggling. She just wasn't ready to listen.

Are you ready to give yourself permission to admit what you know?

You know (even if it is scary to say out loud).
You have strong intuition (even if it is quiet).
You can sense the truth (even if it is uncomfortable).

You no longer have to be the accommodating good girl who denies her own truth to make people comfortable. It's okay for people to be uncomfortable around you. It might even be good for them to have their feathers ruffled by you. Who knows?

All I know is when you listen to—and trust—your intuition, your life will move smoother than when you don't.

———————————

Fundamentally, our intuition lay in our bodies, while our cultural conditioning lay in our minds.

I was asked a great question while teaching this concept, "Is my body always right? What if my mind has thoughts that are contradictory to what my body says?"

Here's my take: Your body knows what direction in which to go. Your mind knows how.

Our bodies are good at giving us the basics: yes/no, less/more, like/dislike.
Our brains are great at the "how"—figuring out the logistics and practicalities.

The body is the compass, the mind is the sailor steering the ship. Mind + body is more powerful than either as a separate entity.

I remember being in Ghana leading a group of researchers when one of them suggested that we go to Colombia together a few weeks later. My whole body lit up. I felt expansive, warm, open, buzzing. A clear *yes*.

Then my mind kicked online. How? Do I have enough time off? Do I have the resources to do that? All of these logistical questions came in.

If those logistics sweep in too quickly, before your body has a chance to weigh in, your mind will squash the knowing of your body. You will convince yourself you don't know what you know.

Once I felt my body's *yes*, I researched and figured out what needed to happen. Colombia turned out to be a wonderful idea— one of my favorite adventures ever.

The second part of this chapter is not just letting go of our "good girl" conditioning to acknowledge our *yes* and *no*—now our challenge is to express it directly and without apology. This can often be quite scary.

Trigger warning: *The below story contains examples of unwanted touch.*

"My body freezes around him."

Jennifer came to me, because she was struggling to connect physically with her husband. She would tense up when he came near her and freeze when he touched her. She was no longer interested in sex with him.

As we worked together, I discovered he often touched her in ways that didn't feel good. He would tickle her roughly, poke her in the side or try to grab her breasts. She realized this was why she was getting anxious when he'd come near her.

I asked how she responded when he touched her in an unpleasant way. She said on the inside she froze, but on the outside she laughed it off and jokingly told him to stop.

"But he doesn't get it?" I asked.

"No. He keeps going. I hate it."

"Hmm. It sounds as if he isn't understanding you. It may be that your body's laughing and your joking makes him think you sort of enjoy his touch."

Over the course of our time together, she realized she laughed off his touch because she didn't want to hurt his feelings or make him uncomfortable (Hello, good girl conditioning!). So we worked on handing back to him responsibility for his feelings and then paying attention to her internal body signals of *that doesn't feel good* and trusting herself.

Lastly, we explored how to let those signals show on the outside. Instead of pretending unpleasant touch was okay, she began to wince, frown, pull away and ask him to stop.

It worked.

As she became more willing to be honest and more aware of what didn't feel good, her husband came to understand the impact he was having. He realized he didn't really know how to touch his wife and became curious about what types of touch felt good.

From there, she explored her desires—how she DID want to be touched. That resulted in fun, sensual play she enjoyed immensely. Yet to get there, she had to face the uncomfortable truth and be honest with him about what didn't feel good.

Good Girls Don't Say No

Accommodating good girls will try to please people until the ends of the earth, even when it feels terrible. They struggle to say *no*, set boundaries and let people down.

Yet, you are here to practice being a sovereign, powerful woman, not an accommodating good girl. That means it's time to get comfortable with the discomfort of saying *no*.

Many women struggle to say *no* for three main reasons:

1. They don't want to hurt the other person (and thereby feel guilty or like a "bad person").
2. They don't want to lose the love and acceptance of the other person.
3. They have repressed their anger and may not even realize a *no* is needed.

It can be scary to say *no* to someone we love or about whom we care and wonder how this will impact our relationship. We may wonder, "Will they reject me? Will they feel rejected by me?"

In those places, it is helpful to be gentle and self-compassionate with ourselves. By monitoring our self-talk and soothing our fears, we can teach ourselves to become comfortable with saying *no*.

Gentle self-talk may sound like ...

- "I am allowed to say no."
- "I am safe and loved."
- "I have a right to my own space."
- "I don't have to share if I don't want to."
- "My body, my choice."
- "I am doing great."
- "My only job is to be honest about what I'm available for."

- "I'm expressing MY truth, not the other person's truth."
- "I am not responsible for their feelings."

This type of inner compassion is helpful for the first two reasons—fear of rejection and not wanting to hurt others. We can remind ourselves that we're responsible for taking care of ourselves and being honest with who we are.

The last reason women struggle to say *no* is that many women have a hard time accessing their anger, so they may not even realize a *no* is needed. In my story with Daniel, I had repressed my anger for so long that I didn't realize how furious those conversations were making me until I hit a boiling point.

It's a practice to continually check in with ourselves, asking, "Am I angry right now? If so, why? What *no* might I be ignoring?"

When we acknowledge and harness our anger in healthy ways, we may feel more capable of creating boundaries and expressing ourselves.

Unfortunately, anger can also be destructive. If our anger turns inward, we will judge ourselves for being a *no* to something, as if only we were a "better woman," we would be able to (or want to) do that thing. We get angry at ourselves for being constantly irritated with our coworkers, for being too tired to help a friend move or for snapping at our children.

Our anger may be pointed outward through judgement of others. This can happen overtly, with criticism or a sneer. Or it can be more covert as we subtly dismiss others. "How dare my neighbor even ask me to help her move? Doesn't she know how busy I am?"

When you hold your anger with dignity and grace, neither by using it against yourself nor against others, anger can give you the raw, hot fuel needed to say an honest, unapologetic *no*!

While direct communication is often the most efficient, it can be helpful to remember that everything we do is communication. There are many subtle ways to express our *no*. For example ...

- If someone brings up a subject about which we don't want to talk, we can change the subject and ask a new question.

- If someone stands too close to us, we can take a step backward and continue moving away until they get the hint or until we decide to be more explicit in our request.

- If we are not interested in a friendship with someone, we can take a while to respond to their messages or respond with short phrases.

Our bodies, our silences, our faces, and our tones of voice are always saying what we do and don't want. By knowing what we want, we can communicate a cohesive message through our bodies and words.

The following meditation will help you let go of "good girl" conditioning and instead practice checking in with yourself to hear your body's *yes* and *no*.

Meditation: Hearing Your Body's Intuition

Background

This meditation is designed to help go below your mind (where much of our social conditioning to be "good girls" lay), and instead drop into your body for guidance. During this meditation, you will feel your *yes* and your *no* and more clearly listen to your body.

It's especially powerful to do this meditation before making a big decision such as accepting a new job or moving cities, etc. I personally use this meditation when I feel disconnected from my own wisdom. This meditation helps me slow down and listen to the deeper parts of me.

You can find a free audio version of this meditation on my website at **www.megandlambert.com/book**.

Instructions

Find a quiet place where you can sit and close your eyes.

Begin by taking a few deep breaths.
With each exhale, let go a little more.

Bring special attention to your throat, your chest and your pussy—these three energetic centers. Notice if these parts of your body feel open or closed right now, just as you're sitting. Remember: open is soft, relaxed and warm; while closed is tight, cold or tense.

Now, I want you to ask a question where you know the answer is **yes**.

Something simple, such as, "Is my name _____(insert your name)____?"

Notice what happens in your body when you ask that question. You may feel a softening, an opening, a lightness or an expansion, particularly in your throat, chest or pussy.

If you notice nothing, be patient and present. Continue to listen for any clues.

Now, ask another question now where you know the answer is **yes**. Again something simple, such as, "Do I like __(insert delicious food here)___?"

As you ask this question, notice what changes in your body. What parts of you open, soften, become warm?

Take a deep breath to clear.

Now you're going to ask a simple question where you know the answer is **no**. Start with a food you don't like, such as, "Do I like ___(insert gross food here)___?"

Notice your body, particularly your throat, chest and pussy. You may observe these areas tightening or pulling backwards, like a drawing away from the imagined food. You may feel a sense of revulsion, a clenching or a tension.

Whatever your sensations, this is your body's way of saying *no*.

Now, ask a question to which you don't yet know the answer. Frame it as a clear *yes* or *no* question, such as: Do I want to do this program? Should I go on a second date with him? Do I want to kiss her? Do I want to take this job? Am I ready to move to the city?

As you ask your question, notice what sensations you get in your body. Do you feel softening, warming, relaxing? Or tightening, tensing, cold?

The **first** sensation you feel is the one on which to pay attention—before your mind starts weighing in.

If the answer is unclear, you can imagine yourself doing each scenario one at a time and see what happens in your body.

For example, if the question is, *Do I want to go on a second date?*, imagine getting dressed up, getting ready for the date and going out on the date. Then notice what your body feels like.

Then imagine saying, "No, thanks," to the second date and doing something else with your evening. Again, notice what sensations appear.

Remember, you can trust your body's intuition, even if you don't understand it. Often our bodies speak to us only in feelings, symbols, gut instincts...and yet this soul-level wisdom can be incredibly powerful guidance.

Finally, lovingly put your hands on your body as you give your body gratitude for sharing its wisdom. Appreciate your body for the deep well of wisdom it is. When you're ready, open your eyes.

Debrief

How was that for you? Did you get a clear signal from your body?

If you didn't get a clear body signal, that's okay. It can take a while to build trust with your body. Continue returning to this meditation, and over time your body will begin to talk to you. The more you listen and trust your body's signals, the louder those signals become.

Many of us have been taught to live in our minds and to analyze our way through decisions. In addition, due to trauma, stress or pain, we may not have felt safe to inhabit our bodies. So learning how to slow down, quiet your mind and listen to your body may feel new, scary or uncomfortable. Be patient with yourself.

Invitation: Grab Your Journal

1. What "good girl" messages did you receive growing up? What "people pleasing" tendencies have you noticed in your own life?

2. What personal truths have you ignored or repressed in order to please others or keep the peace?

3. Reflect on the last time you felt a clear *YES* in your body. What were the physical sensations of that opening or *YES*? (eg. soft belly, open throat, relaxed hips, etc.).

4. Reflect on the last time you felt a *NO* in your body. What does your body's closing or *NO* feel like? Describe the physical sensations (eg. tight chest, clenched jaw, constricted belly, etc.).

5. Call to mind the last time you ignored your body's wisdom. What happened? Why did you do that? What "good girl" conditioning came up? (eg. moving too fast, people pleasing, trying to look good, overanalyzing, etc.).

6. Often anger or resentment is the first clue that we're trying to please others while violating our own truths. These emotions can be the warning bell that there is an inner *no* to which we aren't listening.

   • What is your relationship to your anger?

   • In what ways is your anger destructive?

   • How could your anger be useful to you?

   (P.S. We go deeper into this topic in Chapter 9 - The Wisdom of Our Emotions)

7. What decisions will you pause and ask your body for guidance on this week?

Exercise: Toddler Tantrum

If you've ever spent time with toddlers, you know they can't help but be 100% themselves. Most of the time, toddlers don't yet have the self-consciousness or social conditioning we do as adults.

When we were toddlers, we knew how we felt and weren't afraid to express it. We let our *yes* and our *no* show. This exercise (hopefully) will give you a glimpse of how you can express yourself unapologetically, like a toddler. We can all use a little more of that toddler magic.

When I did this exercise in my group coaching program, the women were laughing and giggling throughout it. They said this practice made them feel alive. My hope is that it will have a similar impact on you.

This exercise takes only five minutes.

Here's how it goes:

1. Stand up. Preferably in a private place—but feel free to do it in public if you don't mind causing a little scene ;)

2. Exclaim like a toddler: "No! No! No!" Be loud if possible. If you're worried about neighbors, you can yell into a pillow or whisper emphatically.

3. Make fists, jump up and down, pound on the table, stomp your feet, cross your arms.

4. Really let yourself feel and express the "NO!" through your whole body.

5. After a few minutes, change to "YES!"

6. Jump up and down, stretch your arms overhead, wiggle your hips, clap your hands. Channel your inner two-year-old's level of enthusiasm.

7. Let yourself amp up the enthusiasm by 10x. Often we mute ourselves—this is your chance to turn the dial all the way up.

8. When you feel complete, celebrate yourself. You did it! Notice how you feel.

9. Take a minute to reflect or journal on how this experience was for you. What did you get from it? More freedom? Permission? Aliveness?

Now, you don't need to go out into the world acting like a toddler, but hopefully this exercise loosened up some constriction in you so you feel more able to express your honest *yes* and *no*.

Exercise: Expressing Your *Yes* and Your *No*

This exercise is a chance to practice your grown-up expressions, a.k.a. the way you might communicate as an adult with another adult.

You will need a friend for this exercise. This exercise takes about five minutes.

Your friend will ask, "Would you like to go on a date?" Or if that's too awkward, you can also change it to, "Would you help me move houses?"

Practice saying, "No," in as many ways as you can as your friend repeatedly asks you the same question.
Try soft, timid *nos* and intense, angry *nos*.
Be brave and varied in the way you say it.
Notice what saying *no* feels like in your body.

Now, try expressing your yes. Your friend will ask the same question, but this time, the response is only *yes*. Try saying *yes* in many different ways—a hesitant *yes*, a bold, gutsy *yes*, a sexy *yes*, a mischievous *yes*, etc.

As you say *yes*, scan your body. What do you notice? Do you get tight anywhere? Soften? Afterwards, debrief with your friend.

Some questions to reflect on afterward:

- What came up for you when you said *no*?
- What fears emerged? What makes it challenging to say *no*?
- What did saying *yes* feel like?
- What makes it challenging to say *yes*?
- Was it easier to say *yes* or *no*? Why do you think that is?

CHAPTER 3

QUESTIONING OUR STORIES

In the last chapter, we let go of the "accommodating good girl" inside us who denies her body's truth in order to please others. In this chapter, we go a step further to examine all of the old stories we may be carrying from our culture, our family and our upbringing. This chapter will help you become aware of your stories, question them and own your free will.

We will look at: *Who are you?* **And more importantly,** *Who are you NOT?*

We all have stories about what's wrong or right, what's good or bad, what's desirable or repulsive. However, this isn't necessarily our natural, pure essence. So much of what we think is "us" is actually our cultural conditioning, what we've learned from society about ourselves and others.

What's wrong with that?

Inherently, nothing.

As humans, we can't help but make stories. It's how we create meaning out of our world. The problem happens when we (unconsciously) adopt painful or limiting stories about ourselves and life from culture and society. This limits our expression and our free will.

As Dolores, the cunning AI robot from *West World* says quite wisely, *"I didn't believe humans had free will. Turns out, I was wrong. Free will is possible. It's just really difficult."*

This chapter will help you cultivate your free will by creating breathing room between yourself and any inherited stories. This will give you more choice, and in having more choice, you'll become more free. Still with me? Let's go.

The "Selfish" Teenager

Flashback to 2005. I was fourteen years old, sitting in the backseat of my step-mom's black Subaru. I'd been complaining about her being late to pick me up from school. At the end of her wits, she turned around and snapped angrily at me, "You are so selfish and self-centered!"

That shut me right up. My cheeks grew hot. I felt so upset, because to me, being "selfish" and "self-centered" was about the worst insult in the world. And it came from someone I deeply loved and wanted to please.

At the time, I believed only bad people were selfish, and that if I were selfish, it must mean I was bad, too. I didn't consciously understand my story about being "selfish" at the time. No, at the time, I just felt shame and anger.

Reclaiming "Selfish"

Fast forward ten years to when I began doing personal transformation work. For the first time, I examined my beliefs around "selfishness." Why is it so bad to be selfish? What does it even mean to be selfish? What actions or behaviors or attitudes are selfish?

For my whole life, I had taken "selfish" as the ultimate insult, a terrible thing to be. But why? What did this even mean to me?

I challenged my viewpoint further by asking myself, how could being "selfish" be a great thing? How could being "selfish" be exactly what I needed?

For the first time, I realized, "Hmm ... it's 'selfish' to take time to focus on myself to meditate and journal. But it also makes me a better employee and a better friend when I'm feeling more centered and calmer." Maybe being "selfish" is actually a little bit "selfless."

This realization began loosening the grip my old story had on me.

As I continued to study the concept of "selfish," I learned that one of the most common social expectations of women is to give and give and give. We're (implicitly) taught that our value comes from what we do for other people. We intuit that focusing on ourselves and our own self-care is "selfish." Obviously, again, rarely is this story explicitly said, but for many women, it is felt.

I came to realize this fear of being selfish was not inborn. **This fear is cultural.**

As I watch my mom give and give to her family until she gets migraines, or my female coworkers bend over backward to help their male counterparts, or the "mommy shaming" my friend got when she left her baby at home to attend a solo retreat. . .I see woman after woman reenacting our cultural conditioning to put others ahead of themselves.

From that context, being "selfish" became quite revolutionary. As I saw the conditioning placed upon women, I understood my own compulsion to give and give, to never, ever be "selfish." This gave me both compassion for myself AND a fierce determination to rewrite this script.

Repeat after me:

- I am NOT going to be ashamed of taking care of myself.
- I will NOT apologize for following my own desires rather than your expectations.

- My value does NOT come solely from what I do for others.
- I do NOT have to "earn" pleasure by giving to others first.

I'm taking off that itchy sweater of cultural conditioning. I'm giving myself permission to be radically selfish, because after all, this is my own life. What about you?

An Unexpected Friendship

Often our inherited stories aren't just about ourselves—these stories tell us with whom it is and isn't safe to connect, as well as with whom we should and shouldn't be friends.

This fear-based cultural conditioning keeps us separate and isolated. But when we question the stories we've inherited, deeper, more diverse connections become possible.

After university, I lived in San Francisco's Mission District with three great roommates.
The area in which we lived was full of crime, drug addictions and gang violence. My parents were worried about me, but I was fascinated. I had grown up in a middle-class white suburb and felt frustrated by the comfortable, sheltered life there. I craved understanding more diverse lifestyles.

When I moved into the apartment, I noticed a man sitting on my doorstep, with a beer bottle in his hand. He shuffled away apologetically. At first, I was scared of him. I had learned that people that sit and drink on the streets are dangerous, mentally unstable and may hurt me.

I tried to inch past him and scuttle up the stairs to my apartment without talking to him.

But day after day of walking by this man, and day after day of not getting hurt, I began to wonder—is he actually dangerous? Or maybe he's just in pain? Or maybe he's craving human connection?

I wouldn't know unless I talked to him. So one day, I sat down next to him on the steps of my house and introduced myself. He told me his name was Paul.

We chit-chatted for a bit, and as we became better acquainted, our conversation got more personal, and we ended up learning a lot about each other.

He told me he had grown up in foster care in the Midwest. He was put into a dangerous living situation, so when he turned sixteen, he saved up enough money to buy a bus ticket to San Francisco.

As a teenager, he'd had high hopes for a better life here. But he struggled in San Francisco too, and used alcohol to cope with the stress. He'd been in and out of rehab for the past forty years trying to kick his addiction.

I told him about my family, too, how alcohol addiction ran in my family, and how my dad's mom had died of alcoholism before I was born. How many of my aunts and uncles had worked for years to overcome their alcoholism. He nodded. He got it.

We just sat and talked for a while, getting to know each other, sharing our stories. It was an unexpectedly intimate conversation.

From then on, every time I'd pass him, I'd say, "Hey, Paul," and check in. He noticed when I traveled for work and asked me about my trips. I noticed when he wasn't on the steps for a few days in a row, and I'd look around on the streets for him.

Some months he was sober, and we celebrated by sipping water on the steps together. Some months he greeted me on our steps with a bottle of beer. He noticed when I seemed stressed about my consulting work and asked about it. Regardless of what we were going through, we would always check in on each other.

It was a sweet connection, and it was rewriting that story I had that "homeless people are dangerous." Somewhere, I had learned from society to avoid people experiencing homelessness, that they would hurt me. I decided not to give in to that story anymore.

In this moment with Paul, I let go of fear and found a beautiful connection.

As you read this, I wonder if you can begin to sense cultural stories you've inherited about with whom you are "supposed to" connect and with whom you aren't. What did you learn about who was safe and who wasn't? Do you still believe those stories?

The One-Night Stand

The cultural conditioning runs especially deep in our sexuality. We receive so many social scripts around how we should be sexually—along with a heavy dose of shame.

After I broke up with my boyfriend, Daniel, I found myself newly single.

One night, my roommate Erik asked me, "Megan, have you ever had a one-night stand?"

I responded defensively, "No way. Those would make me feel so gross."

He continued teasing me. "Oh yeah? How do you know if you've never had one?"

As a gay man, Erik had spent much of his life questioning his sexuality. He had already "disappointed" his family and had worked hard to break away from society's rules around sexuality, which gave him a freedom that I envied—and also feared.

Up until that point, I'd only had sex with boyfriends with whom I was in love. I'd never had a one-night stand because I was always playing by my programmed sexual "rules" (except for the messy night in Monaco from Chapter 1).

Even as I said, "One-night stands are terrible," I thought, "Wait—whose voice is that?" I realized that was my mom's voice. When I was growing up, my mom told me that every time you have sex with someone, it will go one of two ways. If you love each other, you might feel closer afterward. And if you don't love each other, you'll probably feel empty, terrible and farther away from yourself and from the other person.

So, as I formed my own beliefs (or what I thought were my own), I decided I would never have sex with someone unless I was in love with them. I had all of these rules about what was and wasn't appropriate, such as:

- Only have sex when you're in love and in a committed relationship.
- Don't have too many partners—that makes you dirty.
- When you are in a committed relationship, be sexually adventurous to keep him interested.
- Make sure a man proves his love to you before sleeping with him.

Yet in that moment, talking to Erik, I realized those weren't necessarily *my* rules. My family, society and social conditioning had set those rules. The truth was, I didn't know what my personal guidelines were around my sexuality, because I had never really given myself permission to explore it.

I realized I felt a hunger to explore. With the encouragement of Erik and my roommates, I texted a man I had met the weekend before. The night we met, we kissed and I enjoyed it, so I texted him. *Would you like to meet up again?*

He invited me over to his house. We hung out in the pool and drank a beer. I remember feeling nervous because I had decided to have the one-night stand.

We chatted but weren't really connecting deeply, which was fine because that's what I was looking to challenge anyway. I was curious what it would be like to sleep with someone to whom I wasn't emotionally tied.

We had casual sex, and afterward I looked at him. He was just a human. He was fine, but I wasn't in love with him. I didn't even particularly like him or want to see him again.

It was an odd feeling for the first time to decouple love from sex, to just have sex without an emotional reason or without a commitment.

I left his house right afterward and went home. My roommates, still awake and curious, gathered in the kitchen to ask me about my experience. "How was it?!"

I shrugged my shoulders, "Hmm. I still don't know if one-night stands are my thing. This one was pretty average. But I'm glad I did it. I feel kind of empowered." While I wasn't sold on the experience of one-night stands, I felt proud of my courage to explore this previously taboo behavior. I celebrated breaking my own rules and discovering who I might be without the "rules."

Can you relate?

Now, you don't necessarily need to go have a one-night stand. My invitation is simply to notice the rules or stories you have for your sex and love life and to begin to approach those rules with curiousity.

Often we have deeply ingrained stories around what is "appropriate" or not. Until we stop and question, "Wait, whose voice is that? Do I even believe it?", that voice can sound like "The Truth."

Your particular story may be something like:

- There are no good men.
- Men don't like to do monogamy.
- Everyone cheats.
- I'm too old to date.
- I can't trust the opposite sex.
- I can't enjoy women.

- If I hook up with a woman, that means I'm a lesbian.
- One-night stands are wrong.
- Talking about sex is inappropriate.
- If you sleep with a lot of people, you're dirty.
- You'll get an STI from casual sex.
- My pussy smells gross.
- My pussy is ugly.
- People don't like to go down on me.
- Men want more sex than women do.
- I don't like to go down on other people.
- I only have sex with people I love.
- I'm a slut.
- I'm a prude.

Often these stories are not consciously chosen beliefs. They are inherited, passed down generation to generation, from culture and society.

Part of being a sexually sovereign woman is giving yourself permission to question the stories you've been taught. To hold each belief up to the light and examine it to see what holds true for you. To try out all the things you learned were "bad" and decide for yourself what your own moral/ethical code is.

Yes, this is a messy process. It can be embarrassing or humiliating. But it is also how we grow up as women. When we are willing to experience it all, we can know in a felt, embodied way what feels good to us or not.

Questioning our stories helps us create a psychological boundary from others' opinions, which helps us establish true sovereignty.

Why "Who Am I?" Is the Wrong Question

Often people interested in personal growth ask themselves: "Who am I? How do I find myself?"

This question comes up because we can sense on a fundamental level that we're living far from our inherent nature.

We've grown up with people telling us who we should be, what is right, what is wrong, what is good, what is bad, what we're supposed to do, what a good life looks like, what a good wife looks like... These outside opinions have pulled us away from our body's natural impulses and desires.

So, really, the question is not so much, "Who am I?" but rather, "Who am I NOT?"

What voices, stories, beliefs, and narratives are running in my mind that I have NOT consciously chosen for myself? What have I inherited from my culture and family without yet questioning?

Without questioning our stories, we are asleep.
We're in our conditioning.
We are in the prison of what we have inherited.
We are not the conscious creator of our lives.
We're following a script.
We're following a hand-me-down life of someone else's expectations.

This chapter is the key to beginning to empty out what is not yours.

What is not your set of beliefs?
What is not your choice?
What is not your story?

By emptying these out, you make space to discover what is left, what is genuinely yours.

Stripping away the paint

At home, we have this large, old table made out of one solid piece of wood. It's covered in a dark stain and paint. I've never particularly liked the table, but I figured it was good enough.

One day, we took a sander and began stripping away layers of dark stain and paint. Underneath, the most beautiful natural wood emerged. Multicolored and luminous, with lines from the years of the tree's life. "That beautiful table was under there the whole time?!" I wondered. Now that I can see the wood's natural beauty, I absolutely love the table.

As humans, we are the same way. We've been painted over by hundreds of different colors of "paint"—the opinions of the people around us and our social conditioning. Restoration is about removing all of those layers of paint to reveal the natural grain of the wood—the pure essence of who we are.

Removing the paint from the table requires heat. So what's the heat that removes the layers covering your essence? Your erotic energy.

As you begin to access your erotic energy, the cauldron of your life heats up, and anything that is NOT you begins to melt off. Over time, the layers that are not you, that were never you, dissipate, revealing what is truly you. Each chapter in this book will help you in that process.

"It's Slutty to Flirt."

Recently, I worked with a client who was trying to get over a controlling ex-boyfriend.

When we started working together, she was single, having just broken up with him. She felt trapped around her sexuality, afraid to move forward to date and possibly to sleep with other men. She said, "Being with other men will make me dirty."

I paused and asked her, "Wait, whose voice is that?"
She realized that was her ex's voice in her head.

He had many strong (controlling) opinions about what was appropriate. Her ex had told her, "It's slutty if you flirt with other men. If you have had sex with a lot of men, that makes you dirty and unmarriageable."

"Do you believe that?" I asked.
"I'm not sure", she responded.

We took out a piece of paper and folded it in half. I asked her to write down her ex's beliefs on the left half of the paper. She wrote out all the voices in her head from him, such as "It's dirty to sleep around." Then I asked her to read each of his beliefs one by one and pause to feel her heart and body. What does she believe? What's true for her? Then I had her write her own beliefs on the right hand side.

Giving herself space to question these beliefs and to separate out his voice from her own, was freeing for her. It gave her a chance to reclaim her sexuality, to clear off some of the shame she had acquired from her last relationship and rediscover her own beliefs.

Forsake All Others

What are you believing that is not yours, that may have been passed down to you, that may be cultural?

When we question our stories, we are questioning our cultural heritage, our religious background, our family's morals and our social group's norms. It can be scary to question these stories, because what if we discover we don't believe the same stories and then we don't belong to the group?

This work is much easier done with other women, because this kind of inquiry can feel scary if you're alone. Often our biggest fear is that we won't belong to our community anymore if we question these beliefs around being "appropriate."

It's helpful to find other people who have questioned their own beliefs and can help you question yours, like Erik from my one-night stand story. This makes it easier to question the stories for yourself.

Questioning our stories is the work of emotional and spiritual adulthood. It is helpful to remember that as adults in our modern society, we don't have to belong to survive. In fact, I've seen that evolving may require a shifting of relationships.

When I began questioning my stories, I felt myself pull away from my college friends and move more toward others doing personal growth work. I just didn't feel the same alignment with that group as before. It was scary and sad to feel the gulf growing in our friendships.

And yet, I continued. What is true to ME? What feels right to ME?

This question fundamentally requires us to "forsake all others" in that we become more aligned with our inner truth, sometimes at the expense of external expectations.

I appreciate the wording "forsake all others" as a biblical marriage vow, because it means putting the relationship ahead of all else. **What would be possible if we treat the relationship we have with our own divine knowing with that much reverence?**

While I have lost some friends on my personal growth journey, I have also discovered deeper, richer and more authentic friendships than I ever thought possible. Sometimes, as we grow into the women we're meant to be, we need to separate ourselves from the old community to discover one that fits us even better.

> *Sometimes, as we grow into the women we're meant to be, we need to separate ourselves from the old community to discover one that fits us even better.*

Meditation: Questioning Our Stories

Background

This meditation is inspired by Byron Katie's methodology *The Work*, which helps us question our stories. It will help you reexamine deeply held beliefs around the erotic, sex and love.

You can find a free audio version of this meditation on my website at: **www.megandlambert.com/book**.

Instructions

First, choose a story that feels deep and perhaps a little troubling to you.

Your story could be:

- Good girls don't sleep around.
- I need to be in love first.
- He only wants me for my sex.
- I can't kiss girls.
- I need his love.
- I'm unlovable.
- I always get rejected.
- I'm not sexy.

Choose one belief now. Once chosen, proceed with the meditation....

Get in a comfortable place where you can close your eyes and take a few deep breaths.

Start by noticing how your body feels. Which areas feel tight? Where are you soft and relaxed?

With each exhale, invite your body to soften a little further and your breath to slow down.

Bring your belief to mind.

As you think of that belief, ask yourself, "Who taught me this belief? Whose voice is this?" It may be from your mom, dad, grandmother, grandfather, priest, pastor, school teacher, etc. Allow any images, words or memories to come to mind. If you don't know where this belief came from, that's okay, too.

Keep softening your body and taking long deep breaths.

Now, ask yourself, "Is this belief true?" Wait for a *yes* or *no* answer to come from your body.

Then ask yourself, "Can I absolutely know this is true?" Again, wait for an answer.

Then consider, "How do I react, and what happens, when I believe this thought?"

Visualize yourself acting according to this belief. What patterns or behaviors come up when you believe this story?

Last question, "Who or what would you be without this thought?"

Let yourself imagine who you would be if you shed this belief. What might you do? Who might you become? Imagine vivid details of how your life might be different without this belief.

It can be scary to imagine who you would be without this belief, especially if it's a deeply entrenched belief that has become part of your identity. Simply notice any fear or resistance that arises, witness it and come back to your breath.

Visualize, just for a few seconds, that you did exactly the thing you think is wrong or bad or inappropriate.

Like for me, the belief was, "I'll never have a one-night stand," so I might picture myself having a one-night stand.

> *Inherited stories left unquestioned can imprison you. However, by choosing to question these stories, you create more possibilities and choices in your life. You become a more active creator of your reality.*

For you, what is the thing you would "never" do? I want you to imagine doing that thing. How would that feel? Who would you be? Become curious about this other version of you that's possible.

Conclusion: Inherited stories left unquestioned can imprison you. However, by choosing to question these stories, you create more possibilities and choices in your life. You become a more active creator of your reality.

Invitation: Grab Your Journal

1. What beliefs do you hold about love, sex and relating? Feel free to use the lists I've provided in this chapter as inspiration.

2. When you hear that belief in your head, whose voice are you hearing? Could it be the voice of your mother, father, pastor, grandmother, social media, etc.? Where did this belief come from? If you don't know, that's okay, too.

3. Now question this belief, using Bryon Katie's process, *The Work*.* Ask yourself:

   a. Is this belief true? (*yes* or *no*)

   b. Can you absolutely know it is true? (*yes* or *no*)

   c. How do you react, and what happens when you believe this thought?

   d. Who or what would you be without this thought? (Take time to envision and describe this—it's a critical step).

*Loved these questions by Byron Katie? Me, too. If you're new to her work, I recommend starting with the book: **I Need Your Love—Is That True?** It's life-changing.*

Exercise: Cross-Examine Your Stories

This exercise will help you play "litigator" on your stories, thereby creating more freedom and space there. This exercise is similar to the one I did with my client above.

1. Choose a story that is holding you back in your love or sex life, such as, "Men don't like to be loyal," or, "I'm too old to date," or, "I can't kiss women." It can also be the same belief from the meditation you just did.

2. Write that story on the top of a blank piece of paper.

3. On the rest of the paper, write out all of the evidence that runs contrary to that story.

    a. Ex: If your story is "Men aren't loyal," you'd list counterevidence such as every man you've met who's loyal, your friends' husbands who are faithful, even men in books or movies who demonstrate loyalty.

    b. Continue until the page is full.

    c. If you get stuck, you can ask a friend for input on evidence.

4. Read your list of counterevidence. Notice how you feel. Did this soften your story, even by just 5%? That's progress.

Side Note: While a simple exercise, this is intensely ego-dismantling work. Notice if you start to feel resistance to this exercise, which may appear as boredom, being checked out, uninterested or sleepy. That is normal! Your ego may not want to do this, because it can be uncomfortable to question these stories, especially those that are part of our identity. But you may find you feel far freer on the other side.

Reclaiming

"*The world is designed to take the wind out of a woman's sails. To fill her with fear about all the ways she is inadequate. We each need the focus and determination of warrior women to fight the tide of self-hatred that comes from living in a culture that devalues us.*"

—Regena Thomashauer, Pussy: A Reclamation

CHAPTER 4

CHOOSING TURN ON

Now that we have cleared out space in our hearts and minds through forgiveness, listened to our body's intuition and started questioning our old stories, we're ready for the FUN part.

This section is about reclaiming our wild, sexy feminine nature. In it, we will explore turn on, desire, pussy, pleasure, emotions, our cycles and more.

Make no mistake—this is rebellious. This is the type of information that had women ostracized, or even killed, only a couple hundred years ago (and still does in some parts of the world). What I'm about to show you is nothing less than how to unleash your full feminine power.

Ready? Here we go.

The Existential Itch

Flash back to being twenty-three. I was living in San Francisco and working as a leadership consultant. I loved my job, facilitating groups and coaching teams, traveling the world and innovating. On the weekends I went to Tahoe with friends, partied in the city, or had picnics in the park. My life was good.

Despite all of these "good" things, I felt a certain itchiness, a restlessness, a vague feeling of discontent, as if there must be more to life than this. At the time, I couldn't quite explain it, but I felt trapped, as if my life was following the norms set out by my family, culture, and community.

Up to this point, my life felt beautiful, and yet...predictable. Polished vanilla. I craved an edgier lifestyle. Who else could I be? Who would I be if I were broke? Or dressed in gothic wear? Or experimented with drugs?

I craved knowing who I was outside the box of my neat life. Where were my gritty edges? Where was my darkness? My hunger? My beast? My messiness? Something was missing.

I was also quite tightly wound—I had insomnia, a mild ulcer and eczema. I remember lying in bed for hours trying to fall asleep, but my overactive mind and itchy restlessness wouldn't let me sleep until well past midnight. During the day, I wore long sleeves to hide the red rashes of eczema on my arms.

Once I visited the doctor because I was worried about my ulcer, and the doctor told me to take antacid pills and chill out. Easier said than done, Doc. All in all, I didn't have any "serious" problems, but clearly my body was displaying the "itchiness" I was feeling inside.

This "itchiness" led me to start seeking more meaning in my life. I voraciously read books like **The Surrender Experiment**, went to yoga classes and eagerly took personal growth courses. I wanted to learn how to relax and find more fulfillment. My desperate search for something more took me down a fascinating, twisted little rabbit hole.

Finding My Turn On

A few months into seeking for answers, I discovered something magical. It was SantaCon, which if you've never heard of it, means thousands of people dressed in Santa costumes bar crawl across San Francisco.

So, I was quite a sight to see in my giant red Santa costume. Walking home, I stumbled across a building with huge mural Venn diagram reading *Wellness* in one circle, *Sex* in the other circle and *Orgasm* in the overlapping section. Over the top of the Venn diagram read cryptically, "We're all connected."

"What happens inside there?!" I wondered, so I walked inside to ask. Awkwardly, I had barged right into the middle of an introductory class for Orgasmic Meditation. The teacher was embarrassed and quickly told me to leave, but not before I saw a flyer for *Turn On San Francisco*, the organization's weekly meet-up.

"I'm going to that," I decided.

The following week, I tried to convince all of my girlfriends to come with me, but they refused, saying it sounded too weird. I was afraid to go alone but eventually my curiosity overcame me and I decided to go solo.

On a cool Thursday evening, all alone, I walked up to a slightly shabby community center in the Mission. My heart was thumping. I felt so nervous. Being quite outgoing, I wasn't usually shy in social settings, but this felt more...strange. Uncertain. Unpredictable. Weird.

I hesitantly entered the room. A small group of people were awkwardly milling around. I didn't know who to talk to, so I busied myself with getting tea. Then the facilitator told us to sit down on cold metal folding chairs so we could play what they called "communication games."

During the first game, we all responded to prompts like:

- If your orgasm were a food, what kind of food would it be?
- What are you secretly angry about?
- What is your most taboo sexual fantasy?

Clearly, these were far more personal questions than I was used to answering in front of total strangers. I was shocked by the openness with which people answered the questions. Me? I felt quite inhibited, afraid of saying something for which I'd be judged.

My highlight of the evening was the second game called "Hot Seats," where one person sits on a chair at the front of the room, while everyone else asks them questions.

I sat in my chair, simultaneously praying I wouldn't get called on to be in the hot seat, and also intensely wanting to try it. Attracted and repulsed all at once. Close to the end of the evening, the facilitator brought me up to the hot seat. I walked up to the hot seat with shaky legs and a pounding heart.

People asked me questions such as, "If you had the whole day to do whatever you want, what would you do?"

I said, "I don't know. I might try to help someone in need."

The next person asked, "Are you a selfless person?"

I said "Yes, I am. I want to do good for the world."

A man with a long dark ponytail asked, "Are you actually selfish?"

And the first thing that popped out of my mouth was a clear, simple, "Yes."

I was shocked by my own admission. While I had questioned the concept of "selfish", I still felt ashamed to be considered a selfish person. I cringed, scared this admission would result in me being judged by the group. But they just smiled and continued asking questions.

> *Turn on is the feeling of being totally in the moment. Alive, vulnerable, exposed, not sure what will happen next, but open to it all.*

My cheeks were hot, my palms were sweaty, my heart was racing, and my belly was full of butterflies. As I got off the hot seat and returned to my usual spot in the circle, I felt sweaty in all the wrong places. . . and yet, I also felt totally alive. Vibrant, electric, buzzing.

I now know this as the feeling of turn on. **Turn on is the feeling of being totally in the moment. Alive, vulnerable, exposed, not sure what will happen next, but open to it all.**

When I left the community center that night, I called a friend and left a voicemail for her saying, "I don't know what just happened but I think my whole life changed."

I was 100% correct. That night was the beginning of an incredible, wild, profound journey down the rabbit hole and into what I affectionately refer to as the "sex cult."

What is Turn On?

The promise of Eros is to become a magnetic woman who can attract what you want. The way you do that is through turn on. Turn on is the sensation of raw electricity, aliveness and sensation in your body. Flushed cheeks, sweaty palms, fluttery belly, thumping heart, fully present, clear mind, tingly muscles... these are all signs of turn on.

> *The promise of Eros is to become a magnetic woman who can attract what you want.*

We feel turned on when we let our bodies deepest *yes* and deepest *no* guide us. Turn on happens when we're trusting our desire and the impulses of our body over anything our logical mind is telling us we should do.

When I teach the concept of Turn On in my classes, people often initially conflate turn on with arousal or horniness. That's not what I mean.

When I say turned on, I don't mean you're thinking about sex, or you're down to fuck or you're dressing in anyone else's definition of sexy. Turn on doesn't even have to be particularly sexual.

No, when I say turn on, I mean ...

- You feel in your sensual body, connected to taste, touch, smell, feel and sound.
- You're in your highest power.
- You are connected with your innate enthusiasm.
- There's electricity and aliveness running through your body.
- Your emotions are moving freely through you.
- You can reach for pleasure, even when it's difficult.

You know you're turned on when you can feel your body; you feel buzzy, tingly, warm, sweaty, or flushed; and you feel alive.

As one of my favorite teachers, Mama Gena, says, *"So you can see that turn on is a pathway to power. Unimaginable power. Power that is so sacred, so profound, that in certain parts of the world, connecting deeply and intimately with a woman's body was akin to enlightenment."*

That's the power of our turn on.

Ways my clients describe their experiences of turn on:

- openness and energy expanding outward
- an upward flow of vitality
- feeling tingly and alive
- feeling playful, mischievous and flirty
- feeling tingly in their pussy and smiling

One woman described turn on as, *"It's like when you have great sex, and then you go outside, and you have that mischievous smile on your face and you're getting lots of attention and nobody knows why. That's being turned on."* Well said!

To me, turn on feels like warm honey melting across my body and an aliveness starting in my pussy and radiating outwards.

Why Turn On Matters

Turn on connects a woman with her power, with her confidence, with herself.

A turned on woman says, *"I don't give a f*ck what you think I should do. I am doing my own thing. I know my desires and my intuition. I am alive. I am lit up. I trust myself."*

When a woman is not turned on? This is what it sounds like. *"What do you think? Should I do it? I don't know. They want me to do this. Oh, maybe I should do that. I really owe them. I feel guilty."* Quite a different vibe, right?

**Turn on is how we connect to our innate power.
And if we're not owning our power, someone else is.**

When we are not connected to our power, you better believe that we are living a life of expectations, obligations, and people-pleasing. We will feel like victims in our own lives.

> *Turn on is how we connect to our innate power. And if we're not owning our power, someone else is.*

So if turning yourself on feels like a fluffy extracurricular, or if you're like, "I don't have time for pleasure and fun..."

Then this is what I have to tell you:

"Listen up, sister. Turning yourself on is the most important thing you can be doing right now. Because if you are not turned on, nothing in your life is going to feel good. Nothing. You will be living someone else's life, not your own."

The patriarchy tells us that turning ourselves on is an extracurricular, a nice-to-have after we do all of our "real work." That we can prioritize turning ourselves on after we've done enough, earned enough, proved enough to be worthy citizens. Only then we can enjoy pleasure and sensuality and listen to what lights us up.

That conditioning is so completely and utterly backwards. As women, we need to start with our turn on first. Our turn on feeds our own souls...and when we are full and resourced, we can nourish the people around us. When women aren't turned on and nourished, no one gets nourished.

With many of the women I work with, their putting-others-first muscle is very strong. Their doing-good-work muscles are very strong. But their being-flirty-sensual-and-in-pleasure muscle? It is weak and out of practice.

When I recently led the Eros women through an exercise to find their bodily pleasure, every single woman felt a moment of pleasure. **So it's not that we don't know how to feel good—it's that we need permission.** We need to give ourselves permission to believe our pleasure matters, our desire matters, our turn on matters. The first step is permission.

The second step is practice.

Cultivating turn on in your daily life is a practice. It requires noticing your "accelerators"—what *creates* turn on in my life? What makes me feel full of pleasure, vitality and joy?

Conversely, you need to notice your "brakes"—what *kills* the turn on in my life? What makes me feel less lit up and alive?

Our job as radical women who are committed to bold, passionate lives is to take care of our bodies and nurture our turn ons.

Choosing turn on is rebellious

Our society teaches us to turn off, to "grow up," to be "reasonable".

We still live in a patriarchy, with deep conditioning. Many of us have learned that the masculine part of us—our logical, our linear, our rationality—is more valuable than the mysterious, intuitive, body-based, desire-led, sensual part of us.

In the patriarchal world, if you can't quantify it, it doesn't exist. If you don't have proof, it's not valid. If it doesn't make sense, don't do it.

And yet, the feminine is magic and mystery. Your turn on is your feminine connection to God, Spirit, source, your higher self, your soul. Turn on rarely makes sense. To trust your feminine turn on—despite all logical reasoning—is rebellious.

I want you to know that turn on is your natural state. That sexy, erotic, feminine, radiant magnetic, turn on lives inside of you and always has.

Ways to Turn On

After I attended Turn On in San Francisco and learned about the Orgasmic Meditation community, I became more aware of when I was turned on vs. turned off. One day, coming home from my consulting job, I felt my shoulders tight and tense, my mind active, stressing about the next day. On the BART ride, I saw everything that was wrong with the train—it was dirty, smelled like pee and was too crowded. My mind was full of complaints and to-dos.

Suddenly, I had a lightbulb moment. "Oh, this is what being 'turned off' feels like."

Having words for that feeling was helpful. From there, I decided to deliberately turn myself back on.

When I got home, I took a hot shower with essential oils and epsom salt to scrub off the stress of the day. Then I rolled out my yoga mat, lit a candle, and moved through a gentle yoga flow, letting my muscles unwind and soften open. I rubbed sweet scented lotion across my legs, arms, belly, breasts, and hips, enjoying the curves of my body.

I began to relax, to feel more sensations in my body. My mind quieted and settled. I enjoyed the scent of the candle, the feeling of my soft skin. A quiet joy spread across my chest.

"This is the feeling of turn on!" I realized. I felt powerful understanding my own turn on vs. turn off, and what to do to turn myself back on. This felt like a superpower.

What about you? How do you turn on?

Here are a few ways that my clients turn themselves on:

- Connecting with nature
- Working out and feeling their strength
- Taking a hot bath
- Self-pleasuring
- Yoga
- Taking a few deep breaths
- Breaking their own rules
- Doing something outrageous and mischievous
- Traveling somewhere new
- Flirting with strangers
- Seducing their partners
- Being silly and laughing out loud
- Creating beauty
- Getting a massage
- Getting dressed up

- Playing in the garden
- Making art
- Having a heart-to-heart with a friend

There is a common theme amongst all these activities—the absence of stress. Or the absence of all of those voices that say, "I should do this. I shouldn't do this."

A final important note: **turn on spreads woman to woman**. If you're not feeling particularly turned on or lit up, see if you can find time with a girlfriend who is radiant right now. A friend who is enthusiastic about her life, creative in her expression and comfortable in her body.

Let her light inspire you, the same way a lit match can easily light many candles. This is one of the most powerful ways women can depend on each other—to help us remember our own capacity for pleasure and turn on.

Just as important as it is to know what turns you on is to know what is **_killing_** the turn on in your life.

Protecting Your Turn On

A few years ago, I hired an amazing business coach. For most of our sessions, we talked about strategy optimization, email opt-ins, and all the tactics of building an online business. But the best advice she ever gave me was, "**_Megan, protect your vibe like it's your job. Because it is_**."

She was so right. When I am turned on, clients, money and opportunities effortlessly come to me. Life flows almost by magic.

When I get stressed, I crunch down and sit on my laptop for hours, focusing really hard. I start feeling tight and tense all over my back, neck and shoulders. I feel afraid and guilty. Then I wonder why everything in my business feels stuck.

Well, it's because I'm not turned on.

So, I think back to that business coach's advice, "Protect your vibe like it's your job—because it is," and realize the truth in it.

> *"Protect your vibe like it's your job— because it is."*

The word "protect" is important here. Noticing: *What is killing my turn on? And how can I gently remove that turn on killer from my life?*

I was talking with a friend I admire who has carved out a creative life entirely of her own making. I asked her how she managed to build a business that is so **her**, and yet she appears so effortless and relaxed while doing it. She told me, "Megan, I don't do anything that drains me." And I was like, "What? What do you mean? Don't you *have* to do draining activities?"

She responded simply, "No. I either find a way to make the activity not draining, or I delegate it to someone else who doesn't find that task draining. It's not random the activities that are draining to each person. It shows us what each person is created to do."

That line really stuck with me.
"I don't do anything that drains me."

It's become a mantra of mine. Does this sound impossible? Keep reading.

Ending the dinner party

I was hosting a dinner party recently. I was having a delightful time, chatting and laughing. At some point, I realized, "I'm done." I kept trying to be social, because everyone was still at my house. Yet, I could feel my energy and my turn on draining. I just wanted to go to bed.

My mind was saying, "You should wait until people seem ready to go. Or at least wait until the rain stops." But then I heard my friend's voice in my head. "I don't do anything that drains me."

I knew that continuing to socialize would be draining. So, I gathered everyone on the couch for a closing circle. We took turns sharing gratitudes, and then I said, "Well, that was a lovely evening. Thank you for coming. I hope you get home safely."

I felt a little uncomfortable to imply the end of the evening so abruptly, and a few people looked surprised, but one by one they said their goodbyes and went home.

Everyone leaving meant that I got to cuddle up on the couch with my two dogs, watch my favorite TV show, and unwind. I felt grateful, having soaked up the goodness from the dinner party without carrying on out of obligation.

You can say that it is "selfish" to take an action like ending a dinner party early because you're done with socializing. And yet, I believe that if it is not working for me, it is not working for other people. I trust my instincts of when something is "done".

I am curious ... for you, what are you doing right now that's draining your turn on? What bold (or subtle) actions can you take to weaken that drainer?

Pleasure sourcery

When I share this concept, I often hear, "But what about activities I HAVE to do, such as the dishes, filing taxes and caring for my child?"

There are some activities we find draining that are also important for our long-term goals or our overall well-being. For example, I absolutely hate filing my taxes. I find it the most boring, pointless and dull activity on earth.

What do we do in those moments?

We do "Pleasure Sorcery." This means being creative about ways we can make even challenging activities more fun, delightful, saucy or sexy.

How?

For example, with my taxes last year, I dressed up in lingerie, lit a sweet scented candle and made myself a delicious hot cocoa. I set a timer for one hour and promised myself that afterward, I would take a hot bath. When the hour timer went off, I felt accomplished as I went for my soak in the tub. I wasn't quite done yet but I didn't "push through" (which would have been draining)—I set aside another time later that week to finish.

This is just one example.

Other examples:

- Doing sexy kegels while waiting in line at the supermarket.
- Taking your kids to play in a beautiful flower garden rather than staying home.
- Dancing to music while doing the dishes.
- Asking your partner to rub your shoulders as you review your credit card bills.
- Etc.

Your specific situation will be unique, and your "Pleasure Sorcery" will require your creativity in how you can bring delight into difficult situations. How can you prioritize pleasure and turn on, even in the mindset of unpleasant activities?

Sometimes our turn on killers are not so subtle. They can be big decisions we make that crush our desire and our spirit.

Killing My Own Turn On

It was April 2016. I was helping at a weekend course for the community I met through the Turn On San Francisco event. I had come to really enjoy the community and loved learning more about desire.

At the weekend course, the facilitators talked about a week-long intensive happening in June. As soon as I heard, my body lit up.

I got hot and a little sweaty. I knew with absolute clarity that I wanted to participate in that intensive.

I signed up on the spot, paid in full. I trusted my body, and my body was saying YES to this. My friends signed up as well. I felt tingly, alive, excited—and a little nervous. By now, I knew nervous excitement was a good sign. It is one of my hallmarks of turn on.

On Monday morning, I went into the office for my leadership consulting job. My project manager said, "Megan, will you fly to India and lead one of the leadership trainings in June?" My heart sank, because that was the same week as the intensive in which I had just enrolled.

Of course, I could have said *no* to the project leader. That would have been a valid and acceptable response.

But my mind said, *"No, you have to be a good employee and do this. If you don't go, who else will go? You don't need to take that intensive right now—you can take it next time. You should facilitate the leadership training in India."*

Despite the work I had been doing to notice my turn on, my old "good girl" conditioning was creeping back in. That part of me who people-pleases over my desire, who puts others' requests above what I want, who tries to be "perfect" for everyone (remember Chapter 2?).

I turned to my project manager and said, "Yes, of course, I'll go."

My voice said "yes," while my body was saying, "Noooooooooo!"

I felt deflated and numb, like a balloon whose air had just been let out. All of the tingly aliveness I'd had from following my desire to do the intensive was drained from my body.

I tried to console myself. "India will be so fun! A new adventure." While my mind was actively trying to make the situation okay, my body didn't lie. I felt defeated.

A few months later, I was on my flight to India, desperately wondering if I could take a flight back and join the intensive at the last minute. But by this point, the decision had been made. While my friends went off to the intensive, I put on my suit and went to work.

I even gave myself a consolation prize for giving up on the intensive—three days at an ashram. The ashram was a beautiful experience and profound in its own right, but it didn't make up for my original desire to do the intensive. Often, we try to find compensatory actions that are easier than the big desire...but rarely do they actually scratch the itch.
(In Chapter 6, you'll learn why you can never really compromise with your desire.)

After the week ended, my friends came back online after the intensive eager to share how it was. I ignored all of their messages. I didn't want to hear about it. I felt so resentful, angry and bitter that I hadn't been there.

Resentful at whom? Myself. More specifically, I was resentful at the "good girl" conditioning in me that had neglected my turn on desire in order to please others. It felt awful. Not going to the intensive was energetically expensive for me because it caused me to feel turned off for weeks.

Have you ever done something like this?

This is one of the many, many ways we turn ourselves off—by letting external circumstances or logic override our natural desires.

What kills your turn on?

Examples of turn on killers:

- feeling as if we should do something different
- being overly serious
- swirling around in indecision
- asking everyone else for their opinions on our decisions

- feeling stressed out
- engaging in pointless drama
- overwork
- rushing around
- being stuck in our minds
- denying our emotions
- numbing out with alcohol, drugs, food, social media, etc.
- blaming others
- shaming ourselves

In all of these ways, we move away from our bodies' knowing, which kills our turn on.

Turn off happens in a million tiny decisions of overriding our natural impulses, of using our logical brain instead of trusting our desire and following what makes us feel alive. By contrast, turn on happens in a million tiny decisions of trusting our bodies and our desires.

Turn On Begins at the Edge of Your Comfort Zone

One last tidbit about feeding your turn on—turn on is found at the edge of your comfort zone.

If your life currently feels devoid of turn on, try something edgy.

What's edgy for you?

- Traveling to a totally new country?
- Giving your number to a cute person at the coffee shop?
- Taking a BDSM course?
- Admitting your feelings got hurt?

- Wearing a boa down the street or a hot red bra under your business suit?
- Getting your coworkers to have a dance party?
- Texting your crush that you miss them?
- Breaking the rules?

Your edges are unique to you. But I do know you are meant to live near those edges, to touch them gently and notice how much sensation is created when you press into those edges.

So what's your edge? What edgy, exciting activity could you do this week to bring you more turn on?

Meditation: Finding Your Turn On

Background

This meditation is designed to help you feel turned on in an embodied, physical way.

You will be opening up to your body's sensations and welcoming in pleasure. Give yourself at least ten minutes to do this meditation. This exercise is best done in a quiet, private place where you can fully relax. A free audio version of this meditation is available on my website: **www.megandlambert.com/book**.

Instructions

Start by lying down comfortably.

Close your eyes. Take a few deep breaths.

Place both of your hands on your body in a place that could use a little extra love and attention. Maybe you touch your belly, your chest, your throat, your womb or your heart.

Begin noticing what feels good in your body?

Maybe it's the feeling of the bed against your thighs or the soft texture of your skirt against your legs. Maybe it's the soft, relaxed feeling in your belly after each exhale.

What feels good?
Whatever spot of pleasure you find in your body, say, "Yes."

Ideally, you'll say, "Yes," out loud, as hearing your own voice gives yourself permission. If you feel too shy right now, you can also say *yes* in your head.

This *yes* welcomes the pleasure into your body and reminds you, "My body is a safe place to feel pleasure."

Now, let that pleasurable feeling move.

Begin to move your body slowly like a cat waking up from a nap. How does it feel to stretch your arms over your head? Can you wiggle your hips? As you move slowly and leisurely, continue to notice little spots that feel good. Each time you notice a sensation that feels good, say, "Yes."

"Yes."

"Yes."

Breathe.

"Yes."

Take a minute to notice your feet. Does anything feel good in your feet? Maybe you rub them against each other, tickle your toes on the insides of your feet. Feel your thighs. Maybe you press them together and feel the heat between them.

Maybe you touch your hips and caress the curve of your hip, all the while saying, "Yes," whenever you find something that feels good.

Continue to breathe deeply and keep your eyes closed. Let this be an inner exploration. Maybe you touch your breasts gently, caress them and say, "Yes," if it feels good. You can run your hand across your belly and feel the softness of your skin.

Breathe and say, "yes, yes," to each spot of pleasure.

Move slowly. Your body is full of exquisite sensation and nerve endings that require slowness and attention to feel every drop of pleasure of which you are capable.

Remember: your body is allowed to feel good.

Continue to move and wiggle and explore with your hands and your muscles. Where can you find pleasure? Maybe you bring your hands near your pussy, cupping your hand over the top of your pussy, feeling the heat of your hands.

Notice how just the sensation of having your hand near your pussy changes the way your body feels. You may feel a little warmer, a little tingly and maybe a little alive. Just feel and breathe.

Continue moving your body and allow yourself to touch wherever feels good.

Maybe you touch your neck or the nape of your hairline caressing your hair. Give yourself a little scalp massage. Maybe you roll on your belly and touch the curves of your butt. Remember, every time you feel a spot of pleasure, welcome it by saying, "Yes."

Now, come to stillness, placing your hand somewhere on your body that feels good. Take a few more deep breaths. Send your body a little thank you.

Maybe you say something like,

"Thank you for giving me pleasure today. Thank you for housing my beautiful soul, for being the way that I experience the world. Thank you."

When you're ready, open your eyes and journal on the below questions.

Invitation: Grab Your Journal

1. On a scale of one to ten, how much pleasure were you able to access today in the meditation? Ten being ecstatic, full-body pleasure and one being that you felt nothing.

2. During the meditation, what created turn on in your body? Find one thing that created turn on—even if you didn't feel much pleasure.

3. What killed the turn on during the meditation? There likely were some moments when you felt pleasure and some moments you felt nothing. What killed the turn on in your body? Being in your head, judging the experience, not breathing? Just notice.

4. What's something you discovered about yourself and your turn on in the last ten minutes of practice?

The pleasure doctor (that's me) recommends you do this every day, either in the morning or at night before you go to sleep. Pleasure is a muscle that will get stronger the more you practice it. Enjoy.

Exercise: Your Turn On Menu

Sometimes, especially when you feel turned off, it can be difficult to know how to get yourself turned back on. You may not know where to start. This exercise will give you a handy tool to use next time you're feeling turned off.

1. Grab a piece of paper and colorful pens.

2. You're going to make your own "Turn On Menu," so feel free to get creative and artsy here with bright colors, symbols, sticks, glitter...whatever feels festive to you.

3. Create a list of your personal "Turn Ons." Consider what activities...

    a. Delight you?

    b. Make you feel sexy?

    c. Inspire you?

    d. Nourish you?

4. If you need to, refer to the "Ways to turn on" section for ideas.

5. Finish your menu with the statement: "My turn on and pleasure is the fuel for my life. Everyone benefits when I feel great—most especially, me."

6. Enjoy doodling and decorating your "Turn On Menu."

7. Hang your "Turn On Menu" somewhere easily visible, such as your bathroom mirror or bedroom door. Next time you're feeling grumpy, cranky or turned off, "order" something off your menu and do that activity.

8. Have fun!

CHAPTER 5

DISCOVERING YOUR PUSSY

While turn on is not necessarily sexual, there is a connection between the level of turn on you feel in your life and the relationship you have with your pussy. The more you know about your pussy, the easier it is to discover pleasure—inside and outside of a sexual context. Pleasure can be about sex and genitals (sexual) as easily as it can be about the whole body and the five senses (sensual).

Pussy is the birthplace of your erotic feminine, as well as the birthplace of all of humanity. Isn't it strange that colloquially people use the word "pussy" to mean someone who's weak...and yet it is one of the strongest muscles in the human body which has birthed billions of people?

A quick note on gender and physical anatomy. You may identify as a woman and not have a physical pussy. If that is you, I'd like you to imagine an energetic pussy, and feel what you experience through visualization, breath and imagination.

Why I Use the Word "Pussy"

How do you feel reading the word "pussy" over and over again in this chapter? Is it triggering, upsetting, intriguing?

It can be difficult to find a word you like for this part of your body. Many women I work with grew up with no name for their pussy.

No name *whatsoever*. Isn't that crazy? We make sense of our world through language, by having specific words for things. When we don't have a word for something, it can feel as if that thing doesn't exist. So, by growing up without a word for their pussy, many women entirely lost connection with that part of their bodies (until now).

As Mr. Rogers says, "What is mentionable is manageable." If we don't have a word for pussy, if she is not mentionable…well then, our relationship to her is not manageable. So we need a word.

What word, then, to use?

Growing up, I used the word *vagina*. But not only is vagina unsexy and scientific sounding (in my opinion), it is also inaccurate. The vagina is only the inner channel—it doesn't include the lovely labia or the powerful clitoris.

Other women use "cutesy" words such as taco, peach, hoo-ha, va-jay-jay, foo-foo, etc. That feels a little infantilizing to me and doesn't quite capture the sexiness and the power of the pussy.

Tantra uses the word *yoni*, which is Sanskrit. I like *yoni* the most so far, but it still felt a bit unnatural to me as I don't know Sanskrit.

When I heard other women using the word *pussy*, I felt, "Ah yes, that's the word for me." It is a bit edgy, sexy, and taboo—just like my pussy. I also like that pussy has been used colloquially to call someone a sissy or a wuss, as if to be a pussy is degrading. To me, it feels like a feminine reclamation to use that word for one of the most sacred parts of a woman. *(For more on this topic, I love the book: **Pussy: A Reclamation**)*

When I use the word *pussy*, I'm generally referring to the inner and outer labia, mons, clitoris, vagina and cervix.

Your turn! What word do you use (or would you like to use) for that part of your body? Feel free to use any of the words I've mentioned that felt good to you, or ask your pussy directly what she wants to be called.

Throughout the rest of the book, each time I say *pussy*, feel free to insert whatever word you most like for that part of your body.

The Incredible Variety of Pussies

After my eye-opening night at the Turn On event, I continued to connect with the group who organized that experience. They practiced *Orgasmic Meditation* (or more commonly called *OM*), a wellness practice based on conscious sexuality. Of course, at the time I had no idea what *OM,* or *OMing,* meant.

I soon learned the idea behind *OM* is to combine the power of sexuality with the healing of mindfulness. In practical terms, one person strokes a woman's clitoris, very softly, up-down, up-down, for fifteen minutes with no goal except to feel. (And yes, the practice is only done on the clitoris, so no cock stroking or penetration).

I was fascinated by the idea. The concept that you could set aside fifteen minutes to treat sexuality in such a structured way drew my attention. As a newly single woman, I wanted to stay connected to my sexuality, but as I had discovered, I wasn't a big fan of one-night stands. *OM* felt like a safe, fun way to connect with my eroticism.

So, I hired my first life coach, who also taught me *Orgasmic Meditation*. After our initial ninety-minute training, she released me into the wild—a group *OM* experience.

Picture this—thirty men and women gather in a small, brightly lit room in downtown San Francisco to practice *Orgasmic Meditation*. They lay out yoga mats, blankets, and pillows—"the nest," as they called it. I know, that sounds strange, right?

I clung to the edge of the room, terrified by this whole process. My coach urged me, "Go ask someone to *OM* with you. You can do this."

I caught the eye of the young man with the ponytail I had briefly met at the Turn On event. He seemed nice enough and was somewhat cute. Stuttering and blushing, I asked, "Would you like to *OM*?"

"Sure," he said, easily and confidently. Clearly, he was not a newbie like me.

He set up a space for us to do the practice sandwiched between two women. All around me were women of various shapes and sizes. I'll be honest—I couldn't help but look at their pussies.

I was fascinated—I hadn't seen any other pussy besides my own until that day. And now, here I was, practically face-to-face with all shapes of pussies.

> Shaved, waxed, full bush.
> Long labia, invisible labia.
> Bulging and protruding, hidden and tucked away.
> Pink, brown, purple, red, tan.

Why had I never realized how much variety there was in pussies?

Seeing all those pussies was uncomfortable at first, but also so freeing. I realized there were infinite shapes and textures to our feminine parts.

Taken aback by the variety of pussies, I barely recognized when my *OM* partner told me it was time to begin. I laid down and butterflied my legs open as my coach had instructed me.

I was horrified that this stranger was seeing my pussy in broad daylight and sober. What did he think? Did I smell okay? Was I ugly down there? I felt hot and squirmy, flush with shame.

He did the noticing step, where he named something he saw on my pussy. "I notice you have three freckles on your left labia and a light pink color on your inner labia."

What?! I have three freckles? I had no idea. The truth was, I had never really looked at my own pussy up close before. And now, this stranger was describing my pussy better than I could. How weird was that?

We continued with the *OM*. My mind quieted and I felt the rise and fall of sensations across my body. I felt so present, so alive, so completely turned on by this strange experience. While it was clearly a sexual experience, the OM also felt similar to meditation as my whole body settled into the moment.

Afterward, we sat up and shared a favorite moment. Then we went our separate ways with no obligation or chat. What a strangely intimate yet structured experience! I loved it.

Your experience may be different

I share my story with you as an explanation of how I got into the work I do. You may have never tried *Orgasmic Meditation*, nor would you ever want to. The idea of a group experience may freak you out. That's okay! There are many ways to get to know our pussies.

Maybe you're monogamous with your partner and have never looked "down there."
Maybe you've only been with one person sexually.
Maybe you've explored kink or conscious sexuality or group experiences.
Maybe you can't imagine doing any of that.

Whatever your experience is—it is perfect. The point of this chapter is to encourage you to get to know your own body. I also want to celebrate the beautiful diversity of pussies, whether or not you ever see one besides your own. Make sense? Okay, let's keep going.

Time to Take a Look

After that group *OM* experience, when I realized a stranger knew my pussy better than I did, I decided it was time to take a look at my pussy for myself.

When I got home, I set myself up on the floor, locked the door, and took off my pants. I pulled out my phone, and with the camera on selfie mode, I looked at my pussy.

My first thought was, "My pussy is ugly. My inner labia is too long." I felt so stupid, awkward and foolish doing this. I realized I'd grown up as a feminist, yet somewhere along the way, I got disconnected from my feminine body parts. As one client told me, "My private parts were private...even to me."

When I was growing up, no one talked about self-pleasure or getting to know your pussy. The whole topic was avoided. After the day I looked at my pussy more closely, I became curious. What else have I not explored about my body?

I began wondering about pubic hair.

The first boyfriend who ever touched my pussy told me, "You know you're supposed to shave down there, right?"

Embarrassed and shy, I said, "No. I didn't know that. But I will." I talked to my friends and they all shaved, too. I assumed this was the norm. For the next ten years, I shaved my pussy and never questioned it.

I didn't know I had a choice. I was willing to shape my pubic hair to my partner's preferences and never wondered what I might like. (This is the patriarchy in action, by the way, putting a boyfriend's preference over our own exploration.)

After seeing all those women's pussies in the group *OM*, a lightbulb went off. I can have a full bush? Or trimmed bush? Or whatever I want?

So I tried it. I grew out my pubic hair into a big bush. I trimmed down. I tried a landing strip. I tried it all in order to discover: *What do I like? How can I better get to know this intimate part of me?*

Your turn! Have you ever considered how you like your pubic hair? Have you given yourself permission to wonder? Do you know what your pussy looks like?

Why Your Relationship With Your Pussy Matters

The relationship we have with our pussy sets the tone for the way we treat our feminine power. This in turn, sets a precedent for the relationship that our intimate partners will have with us. Let me explain...

Many women grow up feeling their pussies were dirty, disgusting, don't smell good and are ugly. Elective female genital cosmetic surgery (plastic surgery for pussies) is rapidly increasing all over the world. Labiaplasty rates in the United States increased more than 50% between 2014 and 2018 (American Society for Aesthetic Plastic Surgery, 2018, p. 4). I believe this is a combination of the rise of porn, which makes "perfected" genitals appear to be the norm, as well as the patriarchy which trains women to conform to men's expectations for their bodies. This is a challenging climate for any woman to feel good about her pussy.

When we feel like our own bodies, and especially the center of our femininity (our pussies) are ugly, we won't be able to accept adoration from a partner. If we hate the look or feel of our pussies, we will unconsciously block compliments, we will get in our heads if our partners take a good look down there, we will only have sex with the lights off, etc. We can't be open and free in intimacy if we don't have a great relationship with our pussies.

When we are willing to build a relationship with our pussies, we ...

- feel more free in our bodies,

- become more willing to be intimate with our partner(s),
- become more comfortable in our own skins,
- cultivate better intuition,
- and feel more accepting of who we are.

Do you see why the relationship between you and your pussy matters?

By knowing our pussies, we can become more connected to our intuition, and thereby make better decisions. The clitoris is the most sensitive part of the human body. All of that exquisite sensitivity can help us understand what feels good and what doesn't. It's like an early warning system, guiding us away from harmful situations and toward feel-good ones. With our pussy's guidance, we can make better decisions faster and easier, especially decisions around our sex and love lives.

What is good for the pussy is good for the woman. Pussies blossom under mindful, reverent touch. They take their sweet damn time, trusting that their opening happens at exactly the right moment. Pussies love a variety of touches and textures. In many ways, pussies reflect the feminine. So by connecting with our pussies, we can discover how our own feminine side likes to be treated.

Pussies can teach us reverence and patience for our bodies. For example, during self-pleasure, we can ask our pussies before touching or entering them. We can wait until we are fully aroused and ready to move forward sexually. When we treat our bodies with careful listening, we won't let a partner rush us, we won't have painful sex because we aren't yet ready, and we will stop pressuring our pussy to "get off" faster than she wants to. Our pussy gives us a direct experience of practicing our body's *yes* and *no*—and trains our ability to attentively listen.

Pussy Fun Facts

Now that we have a name for this part of our body, let's get to know her.

To start, I highly recommend reading **Women's Anatomy of Arousal**. Sheri Winston describes the pussy in such exquisite, scientific and enlightening detail that I haven't been the same woman since reading it. Truly amazing.

Here's a beautiful image showing the different parts of the pussy from @the.vulva.gallery, an artist who makes educational images of the vulva. Remember: there is enormous variety in pussies—yours may look different than shown below.

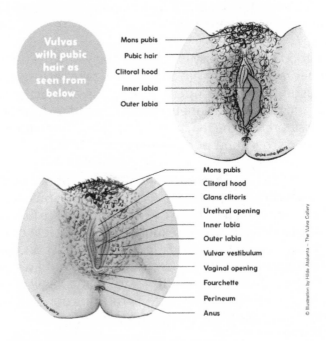

A few facts from that book and others I have read. First, the pussy is the most sensitive part of the human body, period. The clitoris alone has 8,000 nerve endings. No wonder we women are so sensitive!

By comparison, the entire cock, including shaft and head, has only 4,000 nerve endings. We tend to (unconsciously) touch our intimate partners the way we'd like to be touched. Which means that if a pussy owner is touching a cock, she'll often touch it much more gently and softly than the cock owner might want. And when the cock owner touches a pussy, he'll probably touch it more harshly, intensely or directly than may feel good.

This is important to know, because the way we touch each other may be a simple misunderstanding based on having different body parts. Once you know how sensitive your pussy is, it can just be a matter of asking to be touched softer, slower or gentler.

Another fun fact: the clitoris is not just the little pearl-like spot at the top of the inner labia. The clitoris actually has internal "legs" that go down either side of the vaginal opening, which means the entire pussy area—the labia, the clitoris, internal, external—is full of nerve endings, designed to create pleasurable sensations.

Pussies also have erectile tissue. We're accustomed to thinking about cocks getting hard and becoming erect. Did you know pussies do, too?

Pussies **bloom**. Take a look in a mirror as you're self pleasuring. You'll notice that the colors will change dramatically from maybe a light pink or soft brown to a deep, rich red as you become aroused and your pussy becomes engorged with blood. The labia will become more full, velvety and slick. Your whole pussy can open and bloom just like a rose. Amazing, right?

A fun exercise to do here is to touch yourself and notice the ways your pussy changes as you become more aroused. See if you can discover what your 100% arousal looks like. How does it feel to be fully turned on? And note, too, your 100% arousal is a changing target. As you become used to experiencing more pleasure, your 100% will expand and get bigger. We have an infinite capacity for pleasure.

Let's take a look at the internal landscape. You likely know the *G-spot*, which was named after Ernst Gräfenberg, a German physician. I love that in the book **Woman's Anatomy of Arousal**, Sheri talks about how instead of a G-spot, it's a *Groove tube*. Not only is that lovely, since it's not named after a man, it is also more technically accurate. The *Groove tube* is the length of textured, fleshy tissue on the top side of the pussy, closest to the belly.

The "Groove tube" feels different for every woman. I remember trying to find my G-spot and expecting there to be like a button when actually it is more like an area of tissue. You'll know you're close to the *Groove tube* when you start to feel pressure and pleasure simultaneously. For some women it feels as if you have to pee. But when you're highly aroused, pulsing pressure on the *Groove tube* can be quite pleasurable.

Another fun spot is the *A-spot*, which is back toward your cervix at the top part of your pussy. You'll likely need a wand, a toy, or a lover to help you reach the A-spot as it's deeper than most fingers can go. It's up toward the back, around your cervix. This area can feel emotionally charged, sensitive and intensely pleasurable...all at the same time.

In addition to the A-spot, there are amazingly sensitive and pleasurable spots around your cervix. Wait until you're fully aroused to play with your cervix. Otherwise it may feel painful. Emotions tend to get stored in the tissues around this area, as well, so don't be surprised if you begin weeping or feeling angry as you touch around the cervix. If you feel emotions, great! Just keep breathing and feeling. *(More on emotions in Chapter 9.)*

In general, pussies take a little while to warm up. There's real art and patience required when you're touching a pussy. Fun fact: cocks can become turned on quite quickly, often getting hard in only a few minutes. But pussies can take thirty to forty-five minutes before they're fully open and aroused. So, if you've only been having five to ten minute quickies, you may be missing the full power and potential of your pussy (though quickies can be a blast, too!).

Exercise: Take a Look in the Mirror

Background

This exercise is deceptively simple, yet powerful. Within only a few minutes, you could have a profound, life-changing experience. For this reason, I do this exercise in every group program and retreat I run, as well as often with my private clients.

I love hearing the impact this simple exercise has on women. A few examples...

I have seen a middle-aged woman who has never once looked at her pussy finally take a peek and discover herself anew.

I once worked with a woman who struggled with her body image. When we did this exercise, she finally saw herself as a lover might—completely sexy and beautiful. The love she felt for her pussy was so powerful she cried.

Other women are shocked by the mean voices they discover while doing this and realize how deep that patriarchal conditioning runs. The exercise becomes a turning point where they commit to cultivating a better relationship with their pussies.

There are a whole range of reactions, but there's one thing all reactions have in common. If you do this exercise whole-heartedly, even if you've done it many times before, this exercise has the power to change your perspective on your pussy forever.

Instructions

Find a private place where you can relax without fear of interruption.

Lie down comfortably. Take a few deep breaths and invite your body to soften.

Now, cup your hand over your pussy and send a little gratitude and love.

You may say something to your pussy like, *"Thank you for the amazing experiences you've allowed me to have. Thank you for being a core part of me. Thank you for giving me pleasure and keeping me healthy."* Feel free to say this out loud or in your head.

Then, take out a mirror or your phone's camera (pro tip: put your phone on airplane mode so you won't get distracted by notifications).

Now, time to take a look at your pussy. Start by simply noticing. What do you see? What colors, textures, shapes? What folds, creases, or lines are visible?

If you're new to your pussy, see if you can identify the basic parts—outer labia, inner labia, clitoris, and vaginal opening. The diagram earlier in this chapter can help.

Next, find something beautiful about your pussy. Maybe it's the silky soft labia. Maybe it's the delicate curl of a pubic hair. Maybe it's the creamy pink colors or the deep mauve browns. Find one thing that is beautiful about your pussy.

Struggling to find something beautiful? That is okay. Be gentle with yourself, and simply notice any judgments.

Now, I want you to explore your pussy with curiosity. What's one thing you can discover about your pussy that you didn't notice before?

It may be a freckle on the left labia. It might be the shape of your hairs. It may be the way that your inner and outer labia lies against your body. Discover one new thing.

Throughout all this, if any judgments arise, just notice them and let them go. It's normal to feel self-critical while doing this exploration. Many of us grew up in a sex-negative culture. We may often hear judgments about pussies, and then those negative voices appear in our own heads. So if you find yourself judging or criticizing your pussy, simply notice those voices and release them.

To finish, cup one hand over your pussy, feeling the heat of your hand against your pussy. Take a few deep breaths and send again gratitude and love.

"Thank you for the opportunity to see you. Thank you for letting me get to know you. Thank you for the beauty I found."

As you're cupping your hand over your pussy, notice if there's a name that feels good to call this part of your body. What name makes you feel most alive, vibrant, sexy in your body? Maybe it's yoni, peach, pussy, vulva or whatever. Be curious and see what arises.

After you complete this exercise, take a few minutes to journal any thoughts or feelings you had during the experience. What did you learn about yourself? What did you discover?

Meditation: Deep Pussy Breath

This is the shortest, simplest meditation in the entire book. It takes less than one minute. Despite its simplicity, don't be fooled—the *Deep Pussy Breath* can shift your entire mood around.

This breath will help your body relax, soften and open. You can do this breath anywhere—in line at the grocery store, while you're in a work meeting, before going on a date. Nobody will even know you're doing this breath.

Start by feeling the central channel of your body, which is your throat, your chest, your belly and your pussy. Notice what areas feel soft vs. tense.

Then take a deep breath, all the way down into your belly. On the exhale, let your muscles relax fully. Take another deep breath in, expanding your belly downward towards your pelvis. Exhale and let it go.

With each inhale, aim to deepen your breath, so the air pressure gently expands into your belly and presses down into your pussy, as if the inhales are expanding your pussy.

In an energetic way, you are "breathing" into your pussy, by bringing awareness to your pussy as you deepen your breath.

With each exhale, let go and relax your body.

Continue for seven breaths.

Struggling to breathe this deeply? That's okay. Many people habitually breathe in a shallow and constricted way, so it can take time and practice to soften your body enough to breathe into your pussy. Keep the intention to deepen your breath and be gentle with your body as it opens.

Notice how you feel after. Softer? More relaxed? More alive? Feel free to use this breath many times a day to continue strengthening your relationship with your pussy.

Invitation: Grab Your Journal

1. Have you ever looked at your pussy? How was that experience for you?

2. What messages have you received about your pussy, or about pussies in general, from your family, culture, intimate partners, and friends?

3. What word feels good for you to use for your pussy? Does your pussy have a name she prefers?

4. What kind of relationship do you want with your pussy?

5. What will it take to build that relationship?

CHAPTER 6

EXPERIMENTING WITH SELF-PLEASURE

In the last chapter, you took a closer look at your own pussy. I hope your pussy is becoming more familiar to you, and you are cultivating an understanding of how she works.

One of the best ways to cultivate a healthy, thriving relationship with your pussy is discovering what turns her on through self-pleasure. That is what we will focus on in this chapter.

Undoing Patriarchal Conditioning on Self-Pleasure

I grew up thinking self-pleasure was a bit gross, definitely shameful, and honestly, slightly pathetic.

For example, when I was fourteen years old, a friend asked me, "Do you touch yourself?" My first response was, "Ew no. That's what a boyfriend does." Due to implied cultural conditioning, I believed self-pleasure was something only lonely single women did until they found a man (harsh, I know).

The cultural system of the patriarchy requires women to be disconnected from their power and subservient to men. Rarely does anyone overtly state that, but for many of us, that's the implicit cultural script we've grown up to understand.

The fastest way to disconnect a woman from her power is to disconnect her from her body and her pleasure. And the fastest way to disconnect her from her pleasure is by telling her that her pussy is disgusting, and she is sinful if she touches it.

This messaging can be transmitted in subtle ways. For example, many parents discourage their baby girls from touching their genitals. From the time many girls are six months old, they are taught that pleasure exploration is unacceptable. That's deep conditioning to unwind.

Self-pleasure teaches you that your body is your own

Despite what the patriarchy tells you, you are not an object for a partner's pleasure, nor is your pleasure sinful. You will discover that pleasure is your birthright, and you have the capacity to experience exquisite pleasure all on your own. This gives women an unforgettable sense of sovereignty and power.

Self-Pleasuring Class at Burning Man

By this point in my journey, I'd spent nearly a year involved with the *Orgasmic Meditation* community, so I had explored sexually quite a bit. And yet, this next experience certainly confronted me. It may confront you, as well, so I encourage you to read the below story with an open mind.

Along with five close girlfriends, I went to Burning Man, a massive annual pop-up intentional festival. We decided to take a workshop called *Sensual Alchemy* hosted by one of my friends, Lauren. During the workshop, she guided us through exercises to "awaken the seven chakras." After we "woke the kundalini energy" and activated our chakras, Lauren laid down and opened her legs to demonstrate a practice she calls *Peaking*. In it, she stroked her clitoris, up, down, up, down following the peaks and the valleys.

I was a little taken aback by how quickly Lauren went into moaning, orgasming and ejaculating. How did she do that so fast? I felt uncomfortable, awkward and slightly judgmental, but mostly, quite curious.

I was familiar with this type of clitoral stroking from *Orgasmic Meditation*, but somehow it felt so strange and intimate to touch my own body like this. I still had quite a few judgments around self-pleasure.

After watching Lauren, she turned to us enthusiastically. "Now it's your turn! We're all going to do this together."

I looked at my five friends, some eager, some wrinkling their noses. I felt nervous taking my pants off in front of my women friends, as if somehow undressing for a man was fine but for my friends? Weird. And touching ourselves next to each other? Weirder still.

But it's Burning Man, and I'm open-minded, so let's try it.

As we began to touch our clitorses, I could hear the rise and fall of my friend's breaths, the gentle sounds they made. It was both private—with each of us in our own space—and intimate as I sensed their pleasure along with my own. The weirdest thing was how totally natural the whole experience felt. I wondered, "Have women been self-pleasuring together like this for thousands of years?" (I now believe that yes, this has been part of our feminine history, but the kind they don't put in history books).

Afterward, we laughed and shared our favorite moments. It was the strangest bonding experience. Group self-pleasure taught me two important things...

One is that permission spreads woman to woman. As one woman gives herself permission to touch her own body and to feel plea-sure, that gives the women around her permission to explore, as well. Together, we create a field where more is possible.

The second learning is that fundamentally, we are animals, and we can intuitively feel each other. During the workshop, I genuinely felt another woman's pleasure as my own. I felt inspired by her turn on and hearing her pleasure lit my own. This means when one woman allows herself to feel good, without words or any effort, that "feel good" will spread to everyone around her. This is a powerful reason to self-pleasure!

Now, you may (understandably) not feel comfortable doing a class on self-pleasure, yet there may be other ways to weave this concept into your life. For example ...

- Can you talk about self-pleasure with your girlfriends?
- Can you share a few juicy details about your intimate life and see how it can light up other women?
- Can you open up about some of your desires, and notice how that may give the women around you permission to do the same?

These are all ways to support each other's freedom around pleasure and sensuality.

The Shame of Self-Pleasure

When I work with women around self-pleasure, I hear these same shame-based stories over and over and over again:

- Self-pleasure is dirty.
- Touching yourself is sinful.
- If I had a partner, I wouldn't need to touch myself.
- I avoid self-pleasure except to "get it over with."
- I don't "need to" self-pleasure.

If you have any of those scripts going through your head, ask yourself, "Wait, is that my voice, or is that my cultural conditioning?" (If the latter, refer to Chapter 3 on questioning your stories).

Pause and reflect on what you learned about self-pleasure growing up. It may have been overt messages. Perhaps, for example, you were three years old and you put your hand in your pants and someone said, "That's disgusting. Don't do that." Or it may be more subtle, such as no one mentioning self-pleasure at all. From that, you learned that self-pleasure is something shameful, not to talk about.

What did you learn about self-pleasure growing up?

"I feel like a weirdo."

A while back, I was hosting my FemRising retreat, a week-long experience for women to reclaim their desires and sensuality. We were in a coaching circle on sexuality, when one woman said, "I have a secret. I feel like such a weirdo for how I used to self-pleasure. I feel so ashamed." She began crying.

For many of us, self-pleasure comes wrapped in a heavy cloak of shame. Shame grows more shame. Brené Brown, famous researcher on the subject of shame and vulnerability, says:

> "If you put shame in a Petri dish, it needs three things to grow exponentially: secrecy, silence and judgment. If you put the same amount of shame in a Petri dish and douse it with empathy, it can't survive."

With this in mind, I created a safe, non-judgmental space to help her clear her shame. With her agreement, I playfully invited all the women to go around and share the most shameful, taboo-ridden ways that they had self-pleasured.

At first the room felt stiff, awkward and uncomfortable. I encouraged them by starting with my own examples. One by one, the women shared their self-pleasure secrets, and in doing so, everyone began to giggle and breathe more easily.

Curious? Here were some of the ways the women self-pleasured:

- By rubbing their pussy against a table corner
- Humping a pillow
- Using the jacuzzi or bath jets

- With the handle of a hairbrush
- Straddling a vibrating chair
- Rubbing against their fists
- With cucumbers and other vegetables
- and many more!

Amazing, right? Our capacity for pleasure is infinite, as is our creativity in finding new ways to experience pleasure.

As each woman shared, the circle began to lighten. Women started laughing out loud at themselves and (gently) at each other. They got inspired to try new things. They felt turned on by each other's stories. Being received by each other without any judgment was pure alchemy.

The woman who'd originally expressed shame ended the circle laughing until she'd cried, full of mischievous delight. This particular woman couldn't even say the word "pussy" when she started the retreat, and now here she was, unabashedly sharing her most taboo self-pleasure experiences. She looked incredibly lit-up, radiant and free.

When we're willing to share our dark, taboo secrets in a safe and non-judgmental space, we can release years of built up shame and discover profound freedom.

"But I want a partner to do this."

I was coaching with a single woman who was quite resistant to the whole concept of self-pleasure.

She told me, "Yeah, self-pleasure is great and all. I do it when I'm really horny to get it over with. But I feel pathetic. I wish I had a partner to touch me."

"I get it! I felt the same way. Like why bother touching myself? Isn't it better with a partner?" I responded.

"Exactly. I feel stupid doing it." she said.

"Well, I'm curious—what are you making self-pleasure mean? That you can't get a partner? Or that you're somehow 'settling' for your own attention vs. someone else's?"

She replied, "Yes, I guess that's how I feel. Like touching myself is less valuable than someone else touching me."

I followed-up, "When did your own attention become so invaluable?"

She was stunned, "Good point."

Can you relate to this?

I can, yet I have found that self-pleasure cultivates self-awareness and an empowering knowledge of what turns me on. Then, if I choose to, I can share this information with a partner. To play beautiful erotic "music" with a partner, I need to learn to play my own instrument first.

Remember: Women enjoying their own sexuality, rather than for a partner, has been taboo for thousands of years. It's okay if it still feels taboo in your life.

Is Pleasure "Indulgent"?

The other socially conditioned story is that **pleasure is indulgent**. That turn on, desire and the erotic is the fluffy extracurricular stuff you can do once you've done all of the productive, real stuff such as making money and cleaning your house. Do you have that voice in your head, too?

When you examine that as merely a socially constructed story, you have a chance to reclaim your pleasure. Because your pleasure matters. When you feel good in your own body, you feel good to be around. You become a better employee, sister, friend, partner.

It's rebellious to say it matters that you feel good. It's rebellious to prioritize something pleasurable over your endless to-do list and all of the "shoulds." Never forget that every time you choose pleasure and your own turn on, you're starting a rebellion, even if it's a private one.

Pleasure doesn't necessarily need to be sexual. You can find moments of pleasure in slowing down to eat mindfully, feeling the warm breeze on your skin, letting yourself dance just because it feels good, etc. Just as there are many (non-sexual) ways to discover your turn on, there are many different ways to bring pleasure into your life.

When we make time for pleasure, it has a profound impact on how relaxed, how embodied, how open we feel for everything in life, from business to friendships to creativity.

What About Orgasms?

Ah, orgasms. So much shame, intrigue, and fascination lay in this topic.

Many of us live in a goal-oriented society. We spend much of our day trying to get somewhere or accomplish something. So naturally, we may bring that mindset into our erotic lives, as well. What's the goal in our eroticism? For many people, it's orgasm.

The problem with fixating on a goal like orgasm is that it puts enormous pressure on our bodies. One of my teachers described it like this: "Focusing on orgasm is like going to a beautiful symphony and being obsessed with when the cymbals will clash. You'd miss the whole show!"

In addition to "missing the show" of your full erotic experiences, all of that pressure and expectation can cause our arousal to shut down. Many women (according to some estimates, around 10-15%) have never had an orgasm.

Most women (around 75%) don't orgasm through penetration alone. This makes sense, given that many women need clitoral stimulation to orgasm, which penetration may not provide (unless you add in hands, a toy, or certain sex positions).

It's normal not to orgasm, or only to orgasm in very specific ways (e.g. with a vibrator). Putting this in the context of a culture that pressures women's bodies to "perform" helps us to understand why this is.

For a woman to have an orgasm, she must let go of control. She must feel safe, relaxed, fully turned on and surrendered to the experience. Yet for many women, that's not their erotic reality. She may feel pressure to perform, a need to "show" her partner is doing a good job pleasuring her or to fulfill her own expectations. All that pressure is not a formula for orgasmic success.

In addition, many women suffer from sexual trauma and abuse, which may make it feel unsafe to "let go" into an orgasmic state.

So, my advice? Take the goal off the table. Forget about orgasm for now. Ask your partner(s) to not push for you to orgasm, either. Instead, focus on the moment-to-moment sensations, your breath and softening. You may be surprised by what happens!

Meditation: Mindful Self-Pleasure

Background

In this meditation, I will guide you through fifteen minutes of a mindful self-pleasure session.

I highly recommend following along to the audio version of this meditation rather than trying to read and self-pleasure at the same time. You can listen to the free audio version here: **www.megandlambert.com/book**.

During the meditation, you will be invited to touch your body slower than you may normally. When we go slow, it's easier to feel subtlety and allow our body's natural sensitivity to emerge. Touching your entire body in this way wakes up all the nerve endings so your pleasure is full-bodied rather than concentrated just in your genitals.

You may love this meditation, or you might find it confronting. If you feel resistance to this meditation, notice that. What stories or voices are coming up? Refer to Chapter 3 on how to work with these voices.

How often do you do this meditation? First and foremost, I trust your body with the frequency of your self-pleasure practice. If you don't want to self-pleasure, don't. If you want to self-pleasure every day, go for it.

If you like more specific guidance, here are a few recommendations:

- If you haven't felt sexual in a while and want to "wake up" your sexuality, I'd recommend self-pleasuring two to three times per week for at least fifteen minutes. Use the below instructions to begin with, then try different ways to touch yourself.

- If you want to explore the vast potential of your sexuality, aim to do something erotic daily - sensual dance, self-pleasure, peaking, etc.—as well as one to two longer self-pleasure sessions (around forty-five minutes or so) each week where you can go deeper into pleasure.

- If you have a regular sexual partner, I'd still recommend at least once a week of solo self-pleasure where you try new types of touch and textures on your own body. Then, if you want, you can show your lover what you discovered later in the week!

As always, listen to your body. Your body knows what kinds of touch she wants, when and where.

Ready? Let's begin.

Instructions

Set up a private space where you won't be disturbed. Spend a few minutes making the space sensually appealing to you. You may want to light a candle, turn on the heat or the air conditioning, tidy the space, etc. Bring oil with you—coconut oil, almond oil or olive oil all work.

Start by massaging your feet and calves. Maybe pressing your thumbs into your arches or around your ankles. We often live in our heads and one of the quickest ways to ground back down into our bodies is to touch our feet and our calves.

Breathe deeply, using the "Deep Pussy Breathing" from Chapter 6. Continue with this breath throughout the practice.

Move to the top of your head, gently massaging your scalp. Run your fingers across your cheeks, your lips, your earlobes. Gradually move down to your neck, noticing the sensations there.

Rub some oil between your hands, and then massage your shoulders and down each arm. Massage your hands and fingers, paying special attention to the sensitive skin between your fingers.

Massage your legs with the oil, especially your thighs, feeling the muscles there. Touch your hips and if you'd like, turn over, and run your hands across your butt, feeling the curves. Wake up your whole body, noticing any sensations that arise.

Continue to breathe deeply. If there's a spot that feels good, feel free to linger there for a little while.

Massage your belly in slow, clockwise circles, with a steady even pressure.

Now, bring your hands to your breasts and squeeze the entire breast. Use your hands to draw your breasts together, toward the center of your chest, caressing the sides and fullness of your breasts. Then draw slow circles around your nipple with your fingertips, not yet touching your nipple.

As you circle around your nipples, let the circle become smaller and smaller, so eventually you very slowly touch the edges of your nipple. Notice what sensations happen in your body as you do this.

Graze your fingertip across the top of your nipple. Continue circling. You can try up and down motion, left to right, or circle.

Continuing to breathe deeply. If you get distracted by thoughts, just release them and come back to the breath.

As you touch your nipples gently, notice if this activates any sensations in your pussy. You may love this, or you may not. Listen to your body for guidance.

Now, glide your hand from your breasts down your belly, very, very slowly, down to your lower belly. Hover your hand over your pussy, but not yet touching.

Feel the heat of your pussy. The heat of your hand. Relax your fingers against your labia. Noticing if any sensations arise just from that simple touch.

Begin stroking your outer labia, up and down. You can play with gently tugging any pubic hair you may have or brushing it.

Resist immediately going for anything besides your outer labia. The pussy warms up outside-in, so you're giving your pussy a chance to warm up fully before moving forward.

Put more oil on your fingers, then touch your inner labia very slowly, stroking up and down. It may feel good to grasp your inner labia between two fingers. Get to know the soft inner texture of your pussy. Be generous with the oil you use here—more oil will feel better.

Breathe deeply. There's nowhere to get to.

Now, let your fingers travel upwards to where your inner labia meet. At that meeting point, feel for the pearl-like texture of your clitoris. The clitoris may be easy to find, or it may be hidden. Each woman's clitoris is different, but often there's extra sensation in that spot.

You can pull back the hood of the clitoris and touch the clitoris directly. For some women, that's too sensitive. If so, you can touch over the hood. Notice what feels good to you right now.

Stroke up, down, up, down across your clitoris. Feel any sensation in your body as you do this. Be patient with yourself—you may not feel turned on as quickly as you may have expected.

If shame or embarrassment arises, continue to breathe through those feelings. Come back to the physical sensations in your body. If you notice any part of your body getting tense or tight, invite it to soften. Softness is how our body experiences love, and self-pleasure can be a loving act.

Continue stroking your clitoris. Get curious, and try something new. Maybe use your non-dominant hand or a left-right stroke, or a circle stroke.

Slow down your touch so you can feel every little bit of touch. See if you can feel all the curves of your fingertip against your clitoris, maybe even the fingerprint.

Notice if your pussy feels different now than just a few minutes before. What does your pussy feel like when she's a little more awake, a little more alive? Are your lips fuller, more luscious?

If it feels good at this point, you can explore the opening of your pussy, where your vagina starts. Notice what it feels like to bring your finger close to the opening of your vagina. Is there an invitation in your body, or does your vaginal opening feel tight and closed?

Respect the subtle signals of your body. Your pussy will know when she will want something inside of her and when she does not. If your pussy feels tight and closed, continue exploring the outside of your body.

If your pussy feels open and ready, try slipping your finger inside of your pussy, noticing what textures and sensations you discover. You might feel for your G-spot or "Groove Tube". You might play with the different pressures on the left and the right side of the inner walls. If you have a wand or a toy, now is a good time to bring it out.

Continuing to breathe and relax. There's nowhere to get to. If you're used to trying to climax, resist the urge to go for climax, and for now, slow down the stimulation and become curious.

Continue this practice for as long as feels good for you.

When you're ready to complete this meditation, take a minute to reflect on how it felt to touch your pussy today.

> Did you feel moments of pleasure?
> Did you feel resistance?
> Did you feel any shame?
> Did you feel excited?

Reflect on one thing you learned about your body or your pleasure today.

Lastly, place your hand over your pussy and send a little love. Appreciate the pleasure of which your body is capable—both pleasure you may have already experienced and the pleasure you've yet to discover.

Enjoy your infinitely expanding capacity for self-discovery and pleasure.

Invitation: Grab Your Journal

1. What did you learn about self-pleasure growing up? What messages, covert or overt, did you receive from family, culture and media about self-pleasure?

2. How did you feel the first time you self-pleasured, if you did? If you haven't self-pleasured, what resistances do you notice?

3. If you self-pleasure now, how does that feel?

4. What would you like to discover next in your self-pleasure practice?

Remember our capacity for pleasure and eroticism is infinite—stay creative and curious.

CHAPTER 7

TRUSTING DESIRE

As we become more connected with our pussies and our pleasures, we may also notice we feel more desire, both sexually and more generally in our lives.

When we wake up our sexuality, we also wake up our hunger for a passionate, turned on, bold life. The life of our dreams? It is possible when we trust our desires.

Your Desire Matters

What you want is sacred. It is the unique blueprint of your soul, calling you, knocking on the door, asking, "Hello, is anyone here?"

I believe that desire is the voice of Eros, or our feminine soul, speaking to us. It points us in the direction of our unique calling on earth. Desire teaches us how to live fully and bravely and how to become the bold, passionate women we were meant to be.

Consider these two gravestones. Do you want your gravestone to read:

"This is a woman who lived a safe and comfortable life. She did exactly what she was told. She followed all the social scripts. She was an acceptable, appropriate and reasonable woman."

Or do you want your gravestone to read:

"This is a woman who lived passionately and vividly. She let herself yearn and crave and devour everything this world had to offer her. She wrote herself a permission slip to explore every crevice of her desire. She trusted her impulses, receiving fully from life and letting the whole journey transform her into the woman she was meant to be."

Which one feels more appealing to you?

If it is the second one, your desire is the pathway there.

Desire is catalytic

Like a caterpillar turning into a butterfly, you are made for transformation and rebirth. Your desire is the cocoon calling you to dissolve who you are today and be reborn into your next form. In this way, desire is catalytic.

Desire threatens our stable sense of who we are and the certainty upon which we've built a life. For this reason, you will likely resist your desires. Desire can feel so scary, so unknown, that we will often ignore the call.

And yet, here is the uncomfortable truth—your desire is non-negotiable. You don't get to second guess, discount or compromise with your desire. You can ignore your desire for a while, but true desire never goes away. Desire pops up again and again, getting louder and louder until we are finally ready to listen and follow.

Why?

Because desire is your inner voice, the whisperings of your soul. You can no more "get rid of" your desire than you can "get rid of" your nose. Yes, you can cut off your nose, but it will be painful and you will forever feel as if a part of you is missing. It is the same with desire.

Desire cannot be ignored

Don't attempt to "tame" your desire. Often our desires are confronting, big, scary and require our lives to change. So, in response, we may try to appease our desire with a smaller compromise or a tamer solution. That will never work. You will feel resentful, small and unsettled. *(Remember when I killed my desire to go to the intensive, and instead, tried to satisfy myself with three days at an ashram in Chapter 4? It didn't work.)*

While it may be easier in the short-term to ignore our desires, especially the big, disruptive ones, this has serious long-term repercussions.

When we don't follow our desires, it shows. Neglecting our desires hurts our souls. Our hearts close down, our bodies tense up, and our mind sharpens into resentment.

Signs you have been neglecting your desire:

- Being passive aggressive.
- Punishing people for not reading your mind.
- Judging people for not living up to your expectations.
- Feeling closed off and tense.
- Acting like a victim ("Why does this always happen to me?!").
- Settling for mediocrity.
- Feeling resentment of all kinds.
- Feeling vague dissatisfaction or like something is missing.

Nothing feels quite right when you've been neglecting your desire.

Why, then, would anyone neglect their desire? Well, because to live your desire means facing your fears face-to-face. Fears such as:

- Fear of being too much.
- Fear of being rejected.

- Fear of looking like a fool.
- Fear being too vulnerable/exposed.
- Fear of not being met.
- Fear of receiving what we want (Yes, this is a real one! See Chapter 14 for more info ...).

Desire is not here to divide you. You are not meant to fight with your desire, resisting it with all your heart, only to resentfully capitulate in the end. No, you are meant to surrender and trust your desire, letting it lead you where you really want to go.

The art is to surrender to your desire time and time again. Our work is to listen closely to the desire, trust it and follow it into the unknown, again and again for the rest of our lives.

Desire makes us interdependent

I grew up in the United States, where the cultural narrative is the "lone ranger," the "brave cowboy" and the "self-made millionaire." There's a high importance placed on being a rugged individual who can take care of him/herself without needing anyone. For example, women have historically raised children in communities, yet the US narrative reinforces the nuclear family, which leaves many young mothers isolated and struggling.

> **Desire is the antidote to loneliness.**

While that "lone ranger" narrative has some value, it also has significant flaws. I see many lonely, isolated people and many towns where the fabric of community has disintegrated. Desire plays an important role in rebuilding the connection that's been lost.

Desire is the antidote to loneliness.

To follow our desire, we must let go of our armor of militant self-reliance and allow ourselves to become interdependent with other people.

Desire brings us right into the very center of the whirlpool of life, requiring us to lean into community and connection. At its deepest level, desire leads us to the three C's of life—Connect, Create and Contribute.

Any significant desire, such as starting a business, writing a book, having a baby, or moving to a new country—all require us to ask for help, to lean on people who have done this before, to let go of our rigid self-reliance and embrace the humility of our own uncertainty.

When we touch our deeper, soul-level desires, those desires are always a specific, unique way we crave to connect, create and contribute to the world.

Desires are unique

Your desire is like your thumbprint—it is 100% unique to you. You may become inspired by your friend's desire, but you cannot "adopt" hers if it is not true to your soul.

There is a reason some things call to you. A reason your attention gets pulled towards, say, painting rather than playing the guitar. Or maybe you feel drawn toward discovering Africa rather than your hometown. Or maybe you crave the stability of having your own home near your family. Your desire is not random. It is the unique calling of your soul, helping you carve out a life that is custom-made for you. You can trust your desire.

> *Your desire is not random. It is the unique calling of your soul, helping you carve out a life that is custom-made for you. You can trust your desire.*

Instead of following the hand-me-down life of your social conditioning and external expectations, desire helps you create a handmade life that is 100% yours. Beautiful. True.

Why We Settle for Less than Our Desires

Desire can sound all fun and games,
But the truth is,
Desire is terrifying.
Every time you want something,
You open yourself up equally to experiencing fear.

For example …
You have a strong desire to find your life partner.
You can envision being with them, how good it would feel.
The cozy nights cuddled up, the sweet love notes.
The sexy moments together, the tender times.
Your whole body lights up thinking about this desired partnership.

But with that desire comes equal parts fear and resistance.
You inner voices might say,
"I don't want to give up my freedom and independence."
"What if I don't find someone in time?"
"I'm getting too old; all the good people are taken."

Thinking about this desired partnership, you may feel equally excited and scared.

When we want something,
We "pick up the stick".
One end of the stick is HOPE.
We WANT something to happen or to have something.

The other end of the stick is FEAR,
Noticing that we DON'T currently have something.
We feel the lack, the absence of what we want.

The two ends of the stick go together.
We cannot WANT something deeply,
Without noticing the lack of that something and the FEAR of not getting it.

For example,

When you want to make more money,
You may become keenly aware that you currently don't have much money.

Or when you want a girlfriend,
You may realize how deeply lonely you are.

In this context, it makes sense that people give up their desire altogether.
Holding *both* their want and their fear is a lot.

So, what do we do instead?
We settle.
We tolerate.
We wait.
We "try."
We become mediocre.

We say things such as:
"It's fine that we only have sex once a month."
"I don't love my job but it pays the bills."
"It's okay that the kitchen is messy. I barely notice it."
"I will write my book once I learn a bit more."

We justify settling for a life that is only half of what we actually want.
So my question for you:

What are you *tolerating*?
And what do you *really* want instead?

———————————

In the most simple terms, there are two ways to live: by fear or by desire. Below is a well-known short story often attributed to the Cherokee Native Americans.

An older woman sits with her young granddaughter. The older woman says, "My love, inside of you there are two wolves fighting a fierce lifelong battle. One wolf is named Desire and she represents creativity, longing and full expression. The other wolf is named Fear, representing doubt, hesitation and terror."

The granddaughter says, "Oh my gosh, Grandma! But which wolf wins the battle?"

The old woman says, "The wolf you feed."

———————————

Now this story is memorable and powerful, yet it denies a simple fact. Desire and fear go TOGETHER. We never have one without the other. They are two ends of the same stick, two sides of the same coin.

However, our mind may focus on just one end of this stick. Often our attention and mental activity is habitually drawn towards fear rather than desire.

For example, imagine you are starting a new relationship. Your thoughts may be consumed with worries such as, "What if he leaves me? What if I get my heart broken? What if this is the wrong person for me?"

This fear-based thinking leaves your body feeling constricted, tight, tense or numb. When consumed by fear, you have less access to your emotions, your sensuality and your intuitive insights—all parts of you that would help you navigate the ups and downs of a new relationship.

Conversely, you could put your attention on the desire end of the stick. For example you might reflect on what you want this new relationship to feel like and be like, what experiences you may enjoy having. You could think about how you want to express affection for this new love interest, or how you want to devote yourself to the partnership.

Focusing on your desire in this way will likely make you feel softer, more relaxed, open and loving. Your body will show the results of this deliberate effort to come back to desire. A woman rooted in her desire, rather than her fear, becomes utterly magnetic. Best yet, rooted in her desire, she feels powerful, capable and free.

To even begin to ask ourselves, "What do I want? What am I yearning for?" gives us access to a different part of ourselves, a part beyond our habitual fear.

Our habitual fear will always be there. Yet asking the question, "What do I want?" begins to open us up to something bigger than ourselves.

That question is like Pandora's box. First, we start with little desires. I want an iced coconut latte. I want a massage. I want to travel. I want to be in nature.

And from there, the desires get bigger and bolder. I want epic love. I want passionate, full-body sex. I want to help others. I want to save the oceans. I want to live in a beautiful home. I want to have a baby. I want to get a divorce.

As we open ourselves up with these small desires, it makes space for the bigger desires to be heard. The bigger desires may feel like an earthquake, causing the ground to rumble and shake beneath our feet.

Often we're too afraid to admit we have any desires at all. When I begin to work with women, I often hear, "I don't know what I want." That is a clever protection mechanism, because if we admit how vast and deep our desires run...well, it would be almost—but not quite—overwhelming.

We would lose control of our perfectly put together life if we admitted what we really wanted.

So, we start small with tiny daily things. "What do I want today?" As we begin to open to these little daily desires, the bigger desires emerge.

Through all of this, the fear goes nowhere. I like to imagine desire as my left bicep muscle and fear as my right bicep muscle. For many of us, we have really strong right biceps of fear. If we begin to work out our left bicep, our desire muscle, we have a completely different experience. And yet, the right bicep of fear does not disappear.

No, both desire and fear coexist. My fear doesn't need to go away or disappear (nor can it). But by putting attention on desire, I help create a space for possibilities, for expansion, for a beautiful life. The question to consider—which muscle do you work out? Which wolf do you feed?

> *My fear matters.*
> *But my desire*
> *matters more.*

My desire is the voice of my soul. Fear is all the conditioning I've inherited and all my evolutionary fears based on survival and tribal belonging. **My fear matters. But my desire matters more.**

Trusting the Desire to Leave My Career

A couple years had gone by at this point. I had lived in several different *Orgasmic Meditation* community houses, working nights and weekends to put on edgy personal growth courses in San Francisco, New York, Los Angeles and London.

By day, I worked as a leadership consultant. This role had been my dream job, allowing me to travel the world (in business class!), teach about leadership to large groups of people and give me freedom to pursue the projects I found interesting. I could not have asked for a better career.

And yet...I felt as if I was living a double life. On Saturday, I was teaching *Orgasmic Meditation* and how to awaken your erotic feminine. On Monday, I shared about how to shift corporate culture and execute the business strategy.

I felt like two different people. The buttoned-up "corporate" part of me felt like an outsider among my alternative lifestyle friends, while the "mindful sexuality teacher" part of me felt like a secret about which I couldn't talk at work. This split personality began to tear at me inside, and I didn't feel as if I could be whole in either place. I felt lonely despite being surrounded by people.

Step 1: Hearing the Desire

I heard the desire to leave my consulting job over a year before I had the courage to take action on it. It began as a quiet whisper of "Not quite this." But my mind quickly overrode that voice because it felt too scary to admit that my dream job wasn't right anymore.

Leaving my career felt so confronting to the life I'd created that I spent much of my time and energy trying to ignore the desire.

I'd persuade myself, "I love my work. I interact with incredible people. I'm paid well and flown all over the world doing what I love. Why would I quit?"

Still, though, I couldn't deny the subtle signs to go. I felt drained after a day in the office. I had to drag myself into caring about new projects. I'd feel a pang of envy when I met someone who had left their corporate career to start their own business.

Between the tiredness at work, the pang of envy, and the subtle nudging, I could feel my desire to leave my corporate job. See, desire is not an intellectual activity; desire is a body-based knowing coming from our pussy, heart, gut. Our body knows what we want—if only we are willing to listen.

Discovering the language your desire speaks is a deeply personal inquiry, like building a symbolic, non-verbal language between you and your own soul. My desire speaks to me primarily in gut feelings. As I shared in Chapter 2, a tense tightness means "not this," while a soft openness means "yes, please." Other times, my desire comes to me in visions during my meditations, almost like recalling a long-lost memory.

Pause to consider:

1. How does your desire speak to you? In visions, gut feelings, words, emotions, sounds?
2. What desires have you heard lately? How did you hear them?
3. What desires are you trying NOT to hear? What are you afraid of?

Back to my desire to leave my work...

The desire kept speaking to me louder and louder. One moment in particular stands out—It was Monday morning and I had just finished leading a big weekend course on *OM*. I was boarding the underground subway to begin my second life as a leadership consultant. Suddenly, I felt sick. I held in my breath and the nausea until the next stop, where I rushed out of the train and threw up into the trash can.

I rarely ever get sick. I had no other symptoms and hadn't felt ill until I boarded the train.

I wrote an email to my manager and team, explaining that I was taking a sick day.

Then I boarded the train to go home. Once home, I suddenly felt completely better. No nausea, no tiredness, no sickness. I stayed home and rested, but I was clearly NOT sick.

What was this?

I believe this was my desire speaking to me.

See, first our desire speaks in a gentle, featherlight whisper of, "What if ... ?" For me, the whisper was my subtle yearning to quit my job and create my own schedule and company. But I didn't have the courage to listen yet, because my desired life felt so far away, like some silly pipe dream.

Then, if we don't listen to our desire the first time, we get hit with a brick from the universe of, "This is NOT it!"

My throwing up on the subway after months of denying my truth that it was time to go was the universe throwing a brick at me. I knew if I didn't listen at this point, the universe would send me a truck.

Luckily, I haven't yet been hit with the "truck" of my desire yet, but I have seen it happen to my clients. For example, one woman knew it was time to leave her job but she didn't, and within three months she ... 1) sprained her ankle, 2) got an eye infection, 3) got pneumonia, and 4) eventually got fired. Once she finally left her job and began on the career path she really wanted, all of her physical symptoms cleared up nearly overnight.

After throwing up on the train, I knew this was a "brick" from the universe. If I didn't listen, it would get worse.

Step 2: Admitting What You Know

It was time to admit to myself the truth I'd been denying for months—it was time to go.

Once you hear the desire, the next step is to **admit** you heard it.

This can be incredibly scary, because this is when fear comes marching in, in its big black combat boots, trying to keep you safe.

At this point, I was terrified of leaving—how would I make money? What would I do? What if I regretted leaving the corporate world but couldn't go back? And worse yet, would I be a nobody without this prestigious job?

After the fear, grief waltzes in. Following your desire requires acknowledging everything you will have to give up to have the desire and mourning the life you're leaving behind.

I remember lying in bed after coming home sick and openly crying because I knew it was time for me to quit my work, and that truth broke my heart. I dearly loved this job. I loved my inspiring colleagues, I loved the freedom and creativity I had. Leaving my job meant giving up all that.

Following the desire is a leap from a life you know into a life you can't yet see. And in that leap, fear and grief may be your unwelcome companions.

I acknowledge that I was able to leave my job due to a certain level of privilege. I had savings on which I could rely for a few months, which not everyone does. That being said, if you feel a similar desire to move beyond your current job, how can you explore it? Could you volunteer on the weekends? Might you cut down your hours or explore a new role within your company? There are always options—if we're willing to trust our desire.

Back to the story—it was time to admit my desire.

At this point, my desire to leave my job was a delicate little tendril. I knew I couldn't tell just anyone what I was feeling or thinking, because the desire was still too tender. An insensitive comment or snide remark could very well turn me away from what I knew to be true.

Yet, at the same time, I knew I needed help trusting this desire. Taking a leap of faith into our desire requires just the right kind of support.

Step 3: Sharing Your Desire With Someone Safe

That afternoon, as I was lying on my bed, finally taking the truth of my desire to leave my job into my heart, I also realized it was time for me to get support. I sent a message to Maddie, my best friend in the company. I shared with her my struggles and my desire to leave the company and asked for her help in making the transition.

Maddie already knew. She'd felt this coming for a while. It's so funny how often people close to us perceive our desire before we are willing to admit it to ourselves.

Maddie was so supportive and encouraging. She trusted that I would be okay without this job. She reassured my fears and encouraged me to dream.

This is important—choose someone who feels safe. Many people are not safe for the tender tiny tendrils of your desire because they have stomped out their own desire. If you present most people with your most vulnerable desire, it is likely they'll stomp on it, too.

For example, I knew if I called my well-meaning—but worried—parents, I'd get unsolicited advice. If I told my manager, he'd try to fix the situation so I'd stay. If I told my (often financially struggling) roommates, they'd question what I'd do for money. In short—there were many people I could have told, but my intuition knew they may not be the right people to whom to talk about the desire.

In this step, you need to find someone who will hold your desire as real, valid and sacred—because it is.

Desire is not meant to be birthed alone—we are meant to rely on each other for support. To live into your desire, you will need to work with the demons of your mind. You cannot do this work alone. This is why we have community, so we can support each other in living out our desires.

For example, I recently ran into a friend who started writing a book earlier this year.
I asked, "Hey, how's your book coming along?"

She said, "Oh, I stopped writing. I got a little discouraged, and moved onto other things."

I said, "Well, I'm still holding that vision of your book for you. I think it's an important book the world needs to read."
She looked up at me and she smiled.

I don't know if she's going to finish her book, but I do know I am being the kind of friend I want to be and the kind of friend I need in my life. I need friends who hold the brilliance of my desire and remind me of it when I forget.

It's hard to be brave all the time. Sometimes, we need to "outsource" a little courage from our friends. We need someone who will remind us our desire is sacred, special and worth pursuing. We need to hear we are not crazy for wanting what we want. This is the role of your *Desire Doula*, the person who will help you birth this desire into being.

After talking with Maddie, I wrote out an email to the president of our company announcing I would leave in two months. The president wouldn't be surprised, as we had talked about this possibility for months, but still, this email felt solid, formal and real in a way in which none of the previous conversations had. I was terrified to send it.

Maddie stayed on the phone with me as I sent the email. We counted "1, 2 and...3!" When I hit send, we cheered together. After sending the email, I felt vaguely sick, even though I knew the decision was right for me. Maddie's reassurances were so helpful.

Step 4: Showing Up for the Journey

After I hit send on my email to quit my job, I wasn't magically happy, nor did I sail smoothly into the sunset. No, there were a thousand tiny decisions from that moment on about HOW I left the company, WHO I talked to, and WHAT I decided to do next.

Following your desire with grace and elegance takes consistently showing up for yourself and for the people around you every step of the way. It requires mindfulness on the details of transition.

I talked to my London manager face-to-face, my heart thudding. I was so scared he'd try to convince me not to go. Luckily, he encouraged me and told me above all else that he wanted to see me thrive, which gave me a bit of courage.

Next, I talked to my San Francisco manager. He was angry and disappointed. He felt as if he had invested in my growth and I hadn't delivered on that investment by staying longer with the company. I listened and understood, though I was crushed inside. I hated disappointing him and it was uncomfortable to be with his anger. But I knew I needed to stay present with the colleagues I loved and fully hear the impact my decision had on them.

That manager and I worked out a way for me to transfer the knowledge I'd learned over the following two months. I also agreed to work as an independent contractor if projects needed my particular experience. That felt good to both of us.

I believe desire is always ultimately a win-win, and that if a situation is not working for me it is not working for the people around me. And yet, finding that "win-win" can take a little negotiating, patience and understanding. Sometimes at first, your desire may feel like a "win-lose" to the people around you.

There were many uncomfortable moments in the two months of transition. Difficult conversations, sad goodbyes. At the annual Christmas party, I had hoped to be acknowledged for my time in the company, but I wasn't. That hurt, as I didn't feel important. Yet, I also know saying goodbye is awkward and difficult for a lot of people, and there were probably valid reasons why the leadership didn't want to highlight my departure (such as not wanting to inspire other colleagues to consider quitting, as well).

Each of these moments were places when I could have wobbled on my desire, questioned my decision or second-guessed myself. ("Maybe I should just stay.")

A few things helped me stay true to my desire here:

1. **Enlisting support** - by this point, many of my close friends knew I was leaving and encouraged me. They reminded me how fun it would be to work for myself, how creative I could be in starting my own business and reassured me that I'd be financially fine. I leaned on their confidence when my own confidence felt shaky.

2. **Listening to my body's signals** - while my mind often spun out into "what if I stayed" fantasies, my body knew my inner truth. I'd get tight and tense when I thought about staying and relaxed and open when I thought about forging a new career on my own. I couldn't deny my body's gut instincts.

3. **Befriending discomfort** - Law of Attraction people often paint creating the life of your dreams as a big, beautiful adventure—which it is! But in my experience, following your desire also comes with many uncomfortable moments and tough conversations. Can you welcome those sensations, too? Can you befriend discomfort?

4. **Celebrating each step** - Along the way, I celebrated the journey. Leaving London, my last project delivery, my last holiday party, my last day in the office...I celebrated each of these milestones, fully relishing the experience. For example, on my last day in the office, I wore a pink sweater similar to the one I'd worn on my first day at work three and half years prior. I put the photos side-by-side and wrote a post celebrating my time with the company and all I'd learned. Celebrating each step is critical to making a smooth transition.

With every big desire you follow, there will be moments when you wobble and wonder if this is right. The above four tools will help you navigate those wobbles and continue on the journey.

Desires often come in big downloads. An entirely new house. A whole relationship. A big book to write. The big desires can take years to build, and it can be easy to lose hope along the way.

Which is why it is vital to celebrate every chapter written, celebrate every person you help, every dollar you save toward the house, celebrate each movement toward your desire because those celebrations give you fuel.

Five years from now, you'll look back on your life and think, "Wow, look at all that has come to fruition. Look at all of my desires which have ripened into being. Isn't that amazing?"

Step 5: Resting in the Unknown

After my last day in the office, I quietly went home. All the big cel-ebrations were over and it was just me and my inner world. It was December 2017 and everyone headed off for the holiday break.

Over the holidays, my family asked me, "What are you going to do now?! How will you make money? What's your next step?"

"I don't know yet," I responded honestly. I didn't know what I would do next. I didn't know where I would live or how I would make money.

After a big transition like leaving my job, there is a period of time resting in the unknown, a liminal space before the next chapter begins.

After I left my job, I was in the cocoon of the unknown. Inside that space I have learned that my most important job is to rest, talk to my higher power and trust that when it's time for me to know what's next, I will. The puzzle pieces will fall into place when it is time, and until then I rest and surrender.

I slept a lot. I ate nourishing foods. I journaled.

Then a few weeks later, I was visiting my friend Angela at her retreat center, The Land. We were walking around the property. When she asked me what I planned to do now that I'd left the corporate world, I answered, "I don't know."

She said, "Why don't you come live here for a couple of months to help us care for the property?" My body lit up. *Yes.*

When leaving my career, I didn't have a concrete *What's Next* plan. No. In fact, I felt quite lost for almost a year after leaving my career, and before starting my own business.

In my experience, following desire is a bit like driving in the dark. I often can only see a few feet in front of me, only the right next step—and sometimes not even that. It takes an enormous act of faith and surrender to trust my body and my internal wisdom, even when it doesn't "make sense" or add up to a "ten-year plan."

And yet, every time I follow desire, I feel more myself. I create a life that is 100% unique to me, handmade rather than hand-me-down. I can relax knowing that this is MY life, something I have created, guided each step of the way by my own inner wisdom. And that is priceless.

Invitation: Grab Your Journal

1. Fill in the blank: "Desire is _____." Write the first thought that comes to mind, then expand on what you've written.

2. What desires live inside you? What subtle nudges are present in your life right now?

3. Are you ready to admit you've heard the desire?

4. What would you have to give up to have this desire? How does that make you feel? In particular, explore any feelings of fear or grief, remembering these are normal and natural.

5. On whom can you rely for support in this desire?

6. What difficult or uncomfortable moments might arise in following the desire? How will you support yourself during the discomfort?

7. What milestones will you celebrate along the way?

8. What can you do to strengthen your trust and faith in the unknown during this process?

Desire Exercises

Desire is an intimate journey between you and your own soul. This is a life-long journey, repeating again and again every time you feel a new desire. Below are five exercises, each mapping out to one of the five steps I've described above.

Which exercise do you most need right now? Trust your instinct and choose just one exercise to try now. You can always come back and do the other exercises later.

Exercise for Step 1: Hearing Your Desire

1. Find a quiet place where you won't be disturbed.

2. Set a timer for 30 minutes.

3. Close your eyes and let your thoughts settle. One way to do this is to put your attention on the space <u>between</u> things. Between your eyes. Between your fingers. Between your breaths. Between your thoughts.

4. As your mind settles, call to mind all the emotions you want to feel in your desired life. Abundant love. Contentment. Sexiness. Passion. Fill your body with these emotions. Yes, these are manufactured emotions, but they also work. Let yourself enjoy these emotions.

5. Next, let images dance across your mind as you feel these emotions. What pops up? Let yourself be surprised here. Resist grasping on to any particular image, but note which images create sensations in your body. Does one image make your heart sing? Your pussy tingle? Your eyes water?

6. After the timer goes off, jot down any images that create sensations in your body. Don't analyze these images yet. Just let them be for now.

7. As you drift off to sleep that night, let your mind move toward the images.

8. When you wake up, write down a sentence or two regarding what the images mean. What desires might they reveal?

Don't overthink this exercise. The combination of meditating on your desires, welcoming in symbolic images and sleeping on the desires helps you access your subconscious mind. This deeper, subconscious part of you holds clues about that for which your soul—rather than your ego or personality—yearns. You may be surprised by what you discover!

Exercise for Step 2: Admitting What You Know

1. Once you hear the desire (Step 1), the next step is to admit that you heard it and to nurture that desire with your creativity.

2. Take a blank white piece of paper.

3. At the top, write your desire in one sentence. For example: "I want to fall in love," or "I want life-changing sex."

4. Then, close your eyes and envision this desire unfolding. What do you smell, taste, hear, feel, see? Let your imagination be vivid and emerge from your body rather than your mind. Spend at least five minutes visualizing.

5. Afterward, write down as many details as you can remember.

6. If you prefer pictures, you can also draw your desire or find images of the desire online and make a collage.

The most important part of this exercise is to bring gentle love, attention and creativity to your desire. This energizes the desire in the same way water and rich soil energizes a seed.

Exercise for Step 3: Sharing Your Desire With Someone Safe

1. Find someone who feels safe to you. It's best for this person not to be an intimate partner as romance or relationship dynamics may add confusion to this.

2. Once you've selected that person, ask them to meet for coffee/tea or to have a quick phone call.

3. Admit a tiny desire to them. See if they are supportive and if you believe their support is genuine. This gives you information on that person's availability to help hold you and your desire. Not everyone is available for this, and that is okay. Your job is to find someone who is.

4. Then ask if they will help you hold a big scary desire. Ask for exactly the support you need in this big desire. Example requests:

   a. "Would you check on me in a week to see what steps I've taken?"

   b. "Can you cheer me on as I go?"

   c. "Can I share my fears with you just to get them off my chest?"

   d. "I'd love your advice on this."

   e. "Will you encourage me when I get scared?"

   f. "Can I come over for a hug?"

5. Admit the big, scary desire to them.

   a. Important note here: speak the desire as if it can actually happen. There is a world of difference between a timid, "I maybe want this little thing and I know it is basically impossible and crazy, but maybe?" to, "I want this." Be clear and distinct, from your pussy. As Amy Cuddy says in her famous TED talk says, "You can fake it until you become it". Saying the desire in a voice more confident than you actually feel may help you feel more confident.

6. Finally, let yourself graciously receive their support, if it is available.

   a. If they are not available to support you, ask another person for help. It may take a few tries to find the right person!

It makes you incredibly vulnerable to ask and receive support. You did it! Celebrate your courage here.

Exercise for Step 4: Showing Up for the Journey

This is a great exercise for remembering your own brilliance and getting social support as you follow this desire.

1. Invite three to five friends to your house for dinner for a celebration dinner. You can also go out to a restaurant if that feels more festive and doable to you. Feel free to dress up!

2. After the meal has been served, go around the table and share responses to this question: "What is one dream or desire you had which you've already brought into existence?"

3. Give each person a few minutes to share a story of their success. Cheer each other on.

4. Then go around the table to answer this question: "What is one big desire you have right now, and what is one step you've recently taken toward this desire?"

5. Again, celebrate after each person shares. There is nothing quite as motivating as sharing your wins with friends, seeing their excitement, and celebrating their progress too. This can give you the momentum you need to continue following your desire.

Exercise for Step 5: Resting in the Unknown

Following desire is a leap of faith into the unknown. This exercise is designed to help you trust the divine, or that which is bigger than your fear. I use the word "God," but feel free to substitute whatever concept you use—higher power, higher self, unconditional love, angel spirits, the universe, etc. The word matters less than the intention to let go and trust.

1. Imagine the desire you want to create.

2. Ask aloud, "God, please show me what I need to know about this desire. Please send me signs, coincidences or synchronicities to guide me in the right direction." Again, feel free to change "God" to whatever word you use for the divine.

3. Now, let the desire go from your conscious mind. No more analyzing or obsessing about the desire. This is your time to receive guidance.

4. As you move through your day, be on the lookout for signs, symbols, coincidences or synchronicities. Ex: You may notice billboards which draw your attention, songs that come on the radio, particular flowers on the street, animals that cross your path, the current time (11:11!), etc.

5. Trust your intuition on what these signs and symbols may mean for you and for your desire. Your first thought here is best, before you have a chance to overthink it.

While this exercise may feel silly, like believing in fairytales or hoaxes, it can be powerful in strengthening faith. I have seen how much momentum, confidence and encourage-ment people receive when they open up to guidance from that which is bigger than themselves. Give it a try!

CHAPTER 8

SHADOW DESIRES

Just as you become accustomed to following your desire, you may encounter unforeseen obstacles. There is a stage you pass where nothing seems to be happening according to your wishes. Have you lost your manifesting mojo?

No. This is a powerful step in the journey, an introduction to your *Shadow Desires*.

Getting Humbled by Desire

After I left my consulting job, I moved to the retreat center in Northern California named *The Land* to work with my friend Angela. I arrived with a certain arrogance, having worked for years as a high-powered consultant. I'd also spent three years studying desire, practicing turn on and cultivating my eroticism, which gave me some magnetism. Situations usually went the way I wanted, and I had a bit of false confidence.

I was quite unprepared, then, for the work I was to do on the Land. Sensing my false confidence, the Land leadership put me to work cleaning toilets, making beds and cleaning the poop out of the cow trailer.

I felt embarrassed and frustrated. Why was I doing this?

I remember a distinct moment when my friends were in a leadership meeting (to which I wasn't invited), and I was instructed to creep quietly around them, emptying their trash and sweeping their floors. I felt humiliated. Yet, there was an important lesson for me in this work: Can I serve with humility? Can I still matter without a prestigious job?

Growing up, I had tried to *earn* my self-worth through prestigious work, leadership roles and accomplishments. And yet here I was, doing menial labor. If my work was basic, was I still important?

> *Ironically, by striving less to be important externally, I found my own inner sense of importance.*

I realized that yes, I was. Without prestige or status, I was still loved, heard and listened to. Still valuable to the community and to myself. In that realization, I felt free. Ironically, by striving less to be important externally, I found my own inner sense of importance.

Doing menial labor was not what I *wanted*, but it was what I *needed*.

The dark side of desire is the unconscious

Following our desire often sounds quite glamorous, and you may picture fancy cars, beautiful dresses and handsome partners. And yet in my experience, desire can be far grittier, darker and more intense. Desire is as complex and deep as life itself, and following desire requires us to confront our shadows and our shame to bring light to the darkness inside.

Often this "darkness" is our unconscious at work. Desire happens at both the conscious level—those desires we know in our heads—and at the unconscious level—that which is inside us of which we aren't aware.

For example, consciously, I wanted a prestigious role at the retreat center. Yet unconsciuosly, I wanted a role that would help me realize I was important, with or without a fancy job.

To grasp this concept, picture a rider and an elephant. The rider is our conscious mind—he/she knows where we want to go and tries to direct the elephant to go there. The elephant is our unconscious mind—our instincts, our intuition, our repressed feelings and ideas—everything of which we aren't fully aware. The elephant may or may not go where the rider is directing.

It can be extremely frustrating for our conscious mind (the rider) and our unconscious mind (the elephant) to be misaligned. For example, consider a New Year's resolution where you decide you want to eat healthy, work out daily and lose twenty pounds. This is your conscious desire, the voice of the rider.

And yet, three weeks later, you find yourself binging on Netflix, eating a whole box of Oreos and weighing five pounds more. What happened? Well, your unconscious mind wasn't in alignment with your New Year's resolution. You may have had a shadow desire—perhaps for relaxation, sweet foods and the plump cushion of a heavier body.

How do you know if your "elephant" and your "rider" are misaligned? You will know they are misaligned when life doesn't happen according to your (conscious) plan.

> *"Until you make the unconscious conscious, it will direct your life and you will call it fate."* —Carl Jung

When our conscious and unconscious are not aligned, we become shocked by what is happening in our life. We may feel victimized by life, asking ourselves, "Why is this happening TO me?"

(Note: I believe we are active creators in our life, while at the same time there are forces outside of our control such as systematic oppression, traumatic childhoods, sudden

When our conscious and unconscious are not aligned, we become shocked by what is happening in our life. We may feel victimized by life, asking ourselves, "Why is this happening TO me?"

illness and random acts of violence or pain. These events may genuinely happen TO us. I invite you to hold the paradox that we are both creators of our lives AND actors in a larger world that is, at times, unfair, unjust or cruel.)

For the circumstances of our daily lives, though, we have a surprising amount of influence and the ability to create magic when our conscious and unconscious minds are aligned.

> *"The magician directs his magic while the muggle suffers the consequences of his absent-minded magic and then he assigns the authorship of his own magic to external forces."* —OM Rupani

As OM Rupani says, when we are "absent-minded" (also known as when our subconscious and conscious motives aren't aligned), then we still are creating situations in our lives, but we likely blame those situations on outside forces. This is what I mean by *shadow desires*.

For example, if I had a client who struggled to make money despite having plenty of talent and experience. She actively blamed the economy and the lack of job prospects. Yet as we dug deeper into her psyche, we realized she equated money with corruption, so unconsciously she was keeping herself broke in order to feel morally righteous. She often said things about those "corrupt rich people," and so her subconscious was helping her not become one of those people by ensuring she never made much money. Wild, right?

Through this chapter, I'll share how to examine your psyche when it feels as if your (conscious) desires aren't happening, as well as how to uncover and work with shadow desires. Stay with me; this is a complex and intricate yet life-changing topic.

Josh Won't Marry Me

While living at the retreat center, I felt the desire for partnership again. I had spent all of 2017 single and I now felt ready to discover who I was in a relationship.

The retreat center was quite small, with only thirty of us living there full-time. I looked around at my options for a partner and decided I quite liked Josh, the assistant manager. He was rugged, handsome and strong.

Josh and I began dating. The relationship was rocky from the start, with constant fights, hurt feelings and plenty of chaos. Yet, I couldn't deny how exciting all that drama was, and I genuinely loved him, so I stayed.

After a while, we moved to Los Angeles, where I had high hopes of us buying a home, starting a business together and getting married. I was ready to build a life with someone.

I wasn't subtle about hinting toward these dreams, particularly my dream of a romantic proposal. Josh, however, kept telling me he wasn't ready. I took his refusal personally and felt hurt by it. "Why does he not want to marry me? Is there something wrong with me?" In my pain, I angrily lashed out at him.

By this point, I had taught desire to hundreds of people, and yet, here I was with a boyfriend who wouldn't propose to me despite my persistent desire. I tried to put on more pressure by pointing out ring shops and talking about our future wedding. Unfortunately, Josh was consistent in his refusal.

One afternoon, in a particularly cozy and intimate moment, I once again asked Josh if he would propose to me. He conceded. "Yes, let's do it." My mind felt ecstatic! I was getting what I wanted! But my heart felt tight. Something wasn't right.

Day after day, he never acted on what he said. No ring, no proposal. We began to fight more and living together felt miserable. Eventually, Josh moved back to the retreat center while I stayed in Los Angeles. Even though I loved him, I knew I was forcing it. Worst of all, I hated who I was becoming—mean, critical and demanding.

I had made my other desires happen! Why couldn't I get this man—who clearly loved me—to marry me?! I felt ashamed, hurt and confused.

He never did propose, and a few months later we ended the relationship entirely.

At the time, I felt like a failure. I was heartbroken. Now, however, I have deep compassion for Josh and for myself. While my conscious desire was to get married, I could feel a deeper, subconscious part of me saying, "No, this isn't right." I believe Josh's unwillingness to propose was a direct response to the unconscious part of me that felt something was off. Just like him, maybe I wasn't ready to get married, either.

Today, I am so grateful we didn't get married. With the perspective I now have, I know he would have been the wrong life partner for me.

This experience taught me that when life isn't unfolding the way I (consciously) want, there are usually unconscious parts of me that aren't in agreement. This realization is empowering because it means rather than taking the situation personally, I may become more curious—what part of me is not aligned with this desire?

Having Is Evidence of Wanting

The *Orgasmic Meditation* community often said, "Having is evidence of wanting," which at first infuriated me. There was so much I wanted that I didn't have! How could *having* be evidence of *wanting*?

I've come to believe this axiom is (mostly) true.

When all parts of us—conscious and unconscious—want the same thing, we get it. Our "having" of the desire is evidence that all parts of us wanted it.

When we feel blocked in **having** the desire, it is because some part of us doesn't **want** the desire. The trick is to get curious— what part of me **doesn't** want this desire?

For example, I worked with a client who wanted to find a husband but couldn't find any suitable man. She felt frustrated and stuck dating. I asked her:

- What part of you wants a relationship?
- What part of you wants to be single?
- What is the bigger, deeper part of you that can hold both of these other parts?

As she reflected, she realized a conscious part of her was dreaming of partnership.

Yet, a quieter, more subconscious part of her was rebellious, skeptical and wanted to just focus on her business unencumbered by the sacrifices of partnership. That (mostly unconscious) part of her was voracious about "me time" and jealous about spending that precious time with anyone else.

Together, my client and I worked on giving both of these parts of her a voice, so they all felt heard. In holding both voices, we strengthen the "adult" inside of her who can hold contradicting ideas and desires with reverence and patience.

The "adult" part is the bigger, deeper side of us that can hold the paradox of both **wanting** and **not wanting** our desires. When both parts have a chance to speak and be seen, to be heard and understood, then the energy shifts and you are more able to get what you want.

Pretty soon after that exercise, my client found a partner she loves.

> *The purpose of desire is to help us transform into the women we're meant to become. The becoming is the journey.*

Evolving into a woman who can **have** her desires can be a fun process. If you haven't yet attracted what you desire, it doesn't mean that there's something wrong with you. The purpose of desire is to help us transform into the women we're meant to become. **The becoming is the journey.** The exciting part of desire is wondering, "Who will I become as I reach for this desire? How will this desire help me evolve?"

Getting off on the "Not Having"

Imagine craving a piece of chocolate (or insert your favorite food here).
Feel your wanting to taste that chocolate, lick it, touch it, devour it.
Feel your salivary juices churning just at the thought of having the chocolate.
Imagine how good it would feel to slide the chocolate across your lips and into your mouth. Let yourself dissolve into the feeling of wanting.

I'll bet if you actually ate a piece of chocolate right now, it would taste quite a bit more delicious than normal, am I right?

That is the power of our yearning. Our longing has the capacity to energize what we want and make the eventual *having* so much more delicious.

In the gap between the wanting and the having, there is a juicy space full of potential. This space between is damp and full of feminine saturation—if we let it.

If we let it is key, as the gap between wanting and having is difficult for many people.

In that space, you may find yourself ...

- getting frustrated
- demanding to get what you want
- diving into self-loathing about why not having it reflects what a bad person you are
- criticizing the world, God and others for being so unfair

- giving up on the desire entirely
- pretending you don't want the thing, acting nonchalant
- compulsively numbing

Why do we do these behaviors?

Because the gap between wanting and having is full of raw, vibrating electricity. If you aren't used to holding that much yearning you will try to find a way to get rid of it.

What can you do instead?

Get comfortable with the feeling of your own longing, just as we did with the chocolate example in the beginning. Can you allow your wanting to feel juicy, open and trusting?

How?

Well, imagine you want to move into a gorgeous new house but you haven't found the right place yet, nor do you have the resources you need to move. What can you do internally as you search for this new house?

You can ...

a. Hold your desire fiercely yet softly. Picture exactly what you want and have fun imagining vivid details (picture the romantic bathtub you want, imagine the flower garden you'll plant, etc.).

b. Continue opening your body to the desire. Let your yearning for this desire or new home be full, alive, active. Not ignoring or repressing the desire nor getting frustrated (for long), but feeding the desire by staying excited and trusting.

c. Have faith that the universe wants you to have what you want. Remember, your desire is not random or indulgent. Moving towards this desire is part of your evolutionary journey.

d. Take inspired action. Ask the divine for guidance on the right next step. Maybe it's saving part of your income for the new home or telling friends and family what you're looking for. Then take action.

These steps help you more fully enjoy the gap between wanting and having.

Our unconscious desires give a particular pleasure

When we don't have what we (consciously) want, it is because we are having an experience we (unconsciously) wanted. I love the work of Carolyn Elliott, who wrote the book *Existential Kink* and privately coached me for a while. In her book she brilliantly describes the taboo, rich pleasure of our unconscious desires. She writes ...

> *Until you deliberately let your unconscious self fully receive and enjoy and delight in the situation and emotions she's creating (however "fucked up" it may be), that situation will just hang around and stay the same. The scarcity / romantic rejection / self-hatred will stay there because your unconscious will keep just enjoying what she enjoys.*

> *Why? Because you haven't consciously given her the freedom to shamelessly receive and experience the fulfillment of her [shadow] desire...it is through gratitude, deep receiving, and orgasmically enjoying the result you've already created (unconsciously) that you make space for your conscious and unconscious minds to sexually (magically) merge, fertilize each other, and eventually give birth to a new upward spiral of positive synchronicity in your life.* (Elliott, 2020)

When we give ourselves permission to enjoy the creations of our unconscious desires (which feels like "not having" to our conscious mind), we are no longer the victim of circumstance—we are the creators again. As Carolyn Elliott says, in doing so, we make space for our conscious and unconscious to merge, and to create more deliberately together.

The key to this process is to discover the taboo pleasure in your unconscious desires

What does this look like? Let me give you some personal examples ...

- When I launched my first retreat, people weren't signing up right away. Enrollment felt like a struggle. So, I meditated and journaled on why I might be (unconsciously) creating a struggle to enroll people. I realized a part of me wanted enrolling people to be a struggle, because if the process was difficult, somehow the retreat would feel like more of an accomplishment. No pain, no gain, right? As if my suffering to fill the retreat was proving my selfless devotion to the cause and impressive work ethic. After I realized that little unconscious desire, I let myself enjoy the game of suffering to enroll people. Through the enjoyment, something shifted and the retreat sold out. Funny, huh?

- When I went through a period of little revenue early on in my business, I wondered why? Then after quiet contemplation, I realized earning money has always been easy for me, and a part of me craved the constricting pleasure of a tight budget the way some people crave the constriction of a Shibari rope (a Japanese style of bondage rope). So I let myself feel the tight constriction of "not enough money" and let myself (consciously) enjoy the game of money scarcity. After a few weeks of that game, I had my biggest week ever in sales.

- When a man I liked didn't want to commit to a relationship, I let myself enjoy the ferocity that rose up in me and the way I claimed my desire to be in a relationship with him. I let myself enjoy the feeling of passion, conviction and the exciting uncertainty of my invitation. Me relishing each step of our journey—even when it seemed to run counter to my (conscious) desire—created space for him to come back with a fully devoted *yes*.

As you can see, each time, the "not having" was giving me some kind of unconscious pleasure. The key is to find that pleasure and let myself experience it consciously, so the previously unconscious pleasure is brought into the light and fully enjoyed. Some examples of "not having" pleasures:

- You get to feel your yearning more fully.
- You feel superior, as if you're better than others.
- You get to feel inferior and enjoy the hot rush of humiliation.
- You discover your ferocity.
- You "earn" your worthiness through struggle.
- You relish the constriction of scarcity.
- Etc.

I know this can be paradigm-shifting, so let me tell you a little client story on this topic.

Jillian Loves Yearning

While living at the retreat center, I began working with a coaching client, Jillian. At just twenty-four years old, she was a coach in her own right with a thriving business. She was undeniably a powerhouse of a woman who for the most part got exactly what she wanted when she wanted it. Financially successful, independent, popular, with a wide circle of friends, she "had it all."

And yet, as we worked together, I discovered that she had a secret obsession with a male friend of mine. He was in a relationship and not available to date, but that didn't stop Jillian's obsession. Every week during our coaching session, she would talk about him, dream about him, obsess over the last time she saw him and fantasize about seeing him next. She wondered, "Should I make a move on him?!" Then she remembered how damaging that would be for his existing relationship so she'd stop herself.

On and on this went for months. At first, I tried to help her make a decision. Either admit her love for him or move on. She seemed so "stuck" on him.

Eventually, I came to realize something important. **Jillian loves yearning.** As a woman who usually gets what she wants, this man presented a chance for her to feel the gap between her wanting and having. She had a chance to live in uncertainty—will he break up with his girlfriend? Will he want her?

That uncertainty gave her life a certain excitement, drama and intensity that was lacking when she immediately got what she wanted. **The purpose of her obsession WAS the obsession.** It didn't need a solution because she was getting so much juice just by yearning for this man.

So, with a good sense of humor, I talked with her weekly, helping her consciously enjoy her (previously unconscious) creation of this situation. She moved from feeling tortured by the dynamic ("Why am I so stuck on him?!") into relishing the yearning itself.

The yearning had cultivated so much electricity, sensation and aliveness that when she finally saw him in person, she couldn't speak or move. My confident, loud and talkative client was rendered speechless. It was one of the most profound moments of her life.

If you're wondering, then yes, Jillian and the man did get together and have a passionate, beautiful year-long relationship. Yet this story is ultimately about Jillian and her relationship with her own yearning. As she learned to "get off on it" and enjoy the wanting without the having, it created a powerful, profound experience for her.

When Your Desire Becomes Fixated on One Person ...

Have you been in a situation like Jillian?

It's common to get "stuck" on one person, particularly someone who isn't available or someone who is an ex-lover.

Just like in Jillian's story, the key is not to solve your obsession or end the yearning. It is to **enjoy** the yearning. Relish it. Savour it. Be deliciously tortured by it.

> *The key is not to solve your obsession or end the yearning. It is to* **enjoy** *the yearning. Relish it. Savour it. Be deliciously tortured by it.*

Then, you can **learn** from the yearning. Ask yourself, "What do I really love about that person or sexual experience? And what am I learning about my own desire through that?"

These questions help you relate to your own desire directly in its purest form, rather than through a person.

For example, maybe you feel led by this person, and their leadership allows a soft, feminine, surrendered part of you to emerge.

Great! Now you know your true desire is to feel more connected to that soft, feminine, surrendered part of you. From there, you can play with your desire and be creative about how to enjoy it. For example, maybe you take salsa dance classes and relish the feeling of a strong lead dancer who allows you to surrender into the rhythm.

Regardless of how you play with the desire, the point is never to "get rid of" the desire. The desire is never the problem, yet your relationship TO the desire may cause suffering.

For example, if you wish furiously for the desire to go away or you deny the desire for someone it may come out sideways. As Carl Jung said famously, "What you resist, persists." So instead of resisting your desire, what happens if you let yourself fully relish the yearning, the obsession, the raw wanting?

The desire itself is pure creativity and electricity—you may as well let yourself enjoy it.

Meditation: "Not Having" Pleasure

This is Existential Kink meditation, created by Carolyn Elliott, as explained by me, please see her book for the full original explanation.

You can find a free audio version of this meditation on my website at **www.megandlambert.com/book**.

Begin by getting into a comfortable seated or lying down position.

Take a few deep breaths, and notice what your body feels like right now.

Now you can do this meditation by visualization only or you may add the power of self-pleasure by stroking your pussy as you do this. I know it sounds weird to stroke your pussy while thinking of what you do NOT like, but I promise it is powerful. When we bring pleasure to a painful situation of "not having," the situation alchemizes into something else entirely.

Ready to begin? Start by imagining a situation which is not going the way that you want it to.

Maybe you want to make more money than you're making, or you are obsessed with the man who doesn't give you the time of day, or you feel isolated and crave friendship. Choose a smaller situation to work with, such as not getting a raise, rather than a big situation such as your dysfunctional childhood. This makes the meditation more manageable so you can learn how it works.

Imagine the situation that is not going the way you want. See it in vivid detail, imagining the smells, tastes, sounds, sensations and sights of that situation.

Now, tell yourself: "I'm allowed to feel the pleasure of _____ (insert your situation here)." For example, the pleasure of being humiliated, or the pleasure of being in poverty, or the pleasure of being alone.

Notice what sensations arise in your body as you say that.

Do you feel any tingling, warmth or electricity running through your body?

Continue to say similar phrases, such as "I'm allowed to enjoy _____" or "I'm willing to acknowledge that I love _____," filling in the blank with the details of your situation.

Other phrases to try on:

- I don't have to deny my kinky pleasure in this.
- It's safe to admit how much I love this.
- I'm willing to relish this experience.

Notice which statements caused the most sensations in your body. This can give you an indicator of what is most active in your subconscious.

Feel the sensations fully, and allow them to grow and expand as you continue to give approval to these shadow desires. If you feel extra saucy, continue self-pleasuring as you imagine the situation. Notice how the situation may change in tone when combined with increasing amounts of pleasure.

Continue for as long as you like, taking your time to fully relish the "not having" situation.

Notice if you feel resistance to finding any pleasure in this situation, or if your mind is stubbornly insisting the situation is "not good." Just observe those thoughts, thank them and then get curious again—what if there was pleasure in this situation? What would that feel like?

When you are complete, take a few minutes to journal about what you noticed doing this meditation. How have your feelings towards this situation changed?

Fun fact: Researchers from the Multidisciplinary Association for Psychedelic Studies (MAPS) have used the drug MDMA (ecstasy) to effectively treat PTSD (MAPS, 2020). They do this by giving MDMA to patients to elevate their mood and then asking the patient to relive painful memories. The chemically-elevated mood during memory recall rewires the memories so the memories become less painful and the patient suffers less PTSD, even after the MDMA has worn off. I wonder if this is the science behind the above meditation? Worth a guess.

Invitation: Grab Your Journal

1. What is currently happening in your life that you don't like? What desires are you NOT having? (e.g. desire for money/success, desire for a partner, desire for health, etc.)

2. What pleasure do you receive from "not having" this (conscious) desire?

3. Why might your kinky, subconscious self be creating this "not having" experience?

4. When you meditate on that situation and allow yourself to feel pleasure, what sensations do you notice? Be specific and tangible.

5. On a scale of one to ten, how much pleasure did you discover in your "not having" situation? Can you find the beauty in your shadow desire?

6. If you gave yourself full permission to enjoy your "not having" experience, what might be possible?

Exercise: Untangling Your Beliefs

When you are consistently not having a certain desire, it may mean you have entangled beliefs around what it would mean to have that desire. What other beliefs might be attached to this desire?

For example, remember when I gave the example of the client who wanted to make money but struggled to earn much? When I worked with that person, we realized they believed wealth causes moral corruption. She saw rich people as indulgent, selfish and usually immoral. So it made sense that she would (unconsciously) block wealth so she could stay poor in order to feel like a good person.

This is the exercise I took that client through so she could untangle the concept of "money" and "moral corruption" and thereby create more space to imagine herself as wealthy AND morally sound.

Here's how it works:

1. Focus on one desire that holds significant power in your life right now. What do you really want that you do not yet have?

2. Then, ask yourself, "Why might I NOT want this desire?" Make a list of reasons.

3. Review your list and notice which reason has the most sensation in it. Focus on that reason.

4. Notice what two words in the reason that are entwined. Examples:

    a. Being a mother means sacrificing myself. ("mother" and "sacrifice")

    b. Being rich is selfish. ("rich" and "selfish")

    c. Getting married will trap me. ("marriage" and "trap")

    d. Having sex makes me dirty. ("sex" and "dirty")

e. Wanting to be famous is self-absorbed. ("famous" and "self-absorbed")

Note: Often these beliefs are so deep in our subconscious we don't even know they are in there until we start doing this work. You may be surprised by your sentence! And often, these beliefs are not ours—we may have inherited them from society, family or the media.

5. Read the following instructions fully, then close your eyes and let yourself picture this process.

6. Take the two beliefs and imagine them as different colored strings all wrapped up together in a messy ball.

7. Visualize yourself untangling the string. You can use your hands or body as is helpful. Sometimes it's useful to physically move your hands, as if you are untangling something.

8. See the strings as distinct and separate.

9. Surround the strings with a bubble that matches the string color. Ex: "money" as a red string in a red bubble and "morals" as a blue string in a blue bubble. Hold the bubbles apart from each other.

10. Release the bubbles into the world like hot air balloons. Let them both go.

11. Notice how you feel. Notice any new thoughts arising.

12. Imagine each concept as distinct and separate, arranging them in new combinations.

    a. E.g. "I could be rich AND morally sound," or "I could be poor AND morally corrupt."

    b. E.g. "I could be a mother AND not have to sacrifice myself," or "I could sacrifice myself AND still not be a mother."

13. Afterward, take a few minutes to journal about these new statements. How could they be true for you? What new possibilities open up for you when you think in this way?

CHAPTER 9

THE WISDOM OF OUR EMOTIONS

When we trust and follow our desires, we open our hearts up to the full spectrum of human experience. No longer accepting a small life, we undertake the brave journey to move beyond our comfort zones and into the bold life of our dreams. This can create powerful emotions inside of us, some of which we may not yet have learned how to be intimate with.

Our culture tends to chase comfort and avoid pain. Following your desires requires you to move in the exact opposite direction as you open to discomfort and pain in order to evolve into the woman you're meant to be.

Emotions have the capacity to connect us to the knowledge of our deeper wisdom—if we listen. This chapter is about moving from reacting TO our emotions, toward being WITH emotions in order to hear their guidance. It will give you the perspective and tools to be at home with the wide spectrum of human emotions, including the inevitable pain and discomfort of growth.

Unfortunately, many of us were taught to deny or repress our emotions. We learned early on that dark emotions like rage or grief are a burden, something to avoid if possible or move through as quickly as we can.

This cultural conditioning is, once again, the patriarchy at work, teaching us to distrust our feminine emotions instead of learning to listen to them. Emotions are like our internal weather system. Thunderbolts and clouds heavy with much-needed, nourishing rain. Tornados clear away a cluttered landscape. Sunny blue skies. Thick gray clouds. Each emotion or "weather" is here for a reason and it has a lesson for us—if we're willing to listen.

If nature only produced sunny, cloudless blue skies, what would happen to the planet? The plants and animals would dry out and shrivel up. Nothing can thrive in permanent sunshine. And yet for many of us, our culture tries to make us "be happy" and ignore our darker emotions, as if we could live in a permanent state of sunshine.

This chapter helps you dismantle the patriarchal conditioning that says your emotions don't matter, and instead teaches you how to embrace the vivid power of your emotions. Ready?

But first, let's rewind a few decades

It is 1994 and I'm three years old

I'm crying, face down on my bed. I am absolutely devastated, heartbroken, scared. My parents are getting a divorce and my entire world is crumbling. I run to my room, sobbing, kicking the wall, screaming. I hold my teddy bear Fuzzy close.

My well-meaning father comes in. At first he is comforting, but after seeing I'm inconsolable, he says, "Megan, you can choose your emotions. You can be happy if you'd like."

Not great advice for a three year old (or for a thirty year old, for that matter).

He leaves my room. Now alone again, I tell myself to stop crying. I tightly hug my legs and take shallow breaths. "I need to become happy again. It's not okay to be sad," I tell myself. I wipe away my tears and walk outside. I don't say much, only nodding when asked how I am.

From this moment and others like it, the little girl in me believed, "If I want to be loved and accepted, I need to be happy," so I strove to become optimistic, positive and happy. As I grew up, teachers and other parents remarked what a pleasant, polite child I was.

Unfortunately, my darker emotions didn't go away—these emotions went underground into my eczema as I itched my feelings out. My emotions came out sideways as passive aggressive verbal attacks on my brother, controlling behavior toward my friends and a tightness in my body. My repressed emotions buried themselves deep inside my body as tension and uneasiness.

Can you relate? Did you learn to "just be happy," too?

Culture Teaches Us to Deny Our Feelings

I grew up in the United States, where pushy-positive phrases such as, "Turn that frown upside down," or, "You're so much prettier with a smile," and "When life gives you lemons, make lemonade," are common. If you live in the western world, it's likely you don't live in a culture friendly to the full range of your emotional expression.

Yet there are deep, vital, life-giving messages in our dark emotions. If we are to be whole, if we are to be wise and gentle, we must let ourselves feel all of our feelings fully and completely.

Many women were taught that their strong emotions make them seem *crazy*, *hysterical* or *over-reactive*. Our workplaces teach us to be "professional" by appearing to have no emotions whatsoever, only logic and reason (in other words, to appear more masculine). Our intimate partners may tell us to "calm down" or "be reasonable" during intense emotions. Even our personal development books tell us to "think positive" and "focus on gratitude," as if only we were mindful enough we could avoid everything difficult about our human experience.

This is gaslighting. Attempting to convince a woman out of her emotional experience is not only inconsiderate—it is cruel. For when a woman learns to disconnect from her emotions, she disconnects from an essential part of her own truth. Her feminine wisdom comes through by how she feels moment to moment. Without connecting to her emotions, she struggles to trust herself and her decisions. She literally can't feel what to do.

> *Attempting to convince a woman out of her emotional experience is not only inconsiderate— it is cruel. For when a woman learns to disconnect from her emotions, she disconnects from an essential part of her own truth.*

Many of us never learned that each of our emotions have an important role to play and can teach us how to live more fully. This chapter will show you the messages your emotions may carry and help you learn how to trust these messages. By embracing all of your vivid, varied emotions, you will open up to the full colorful spectrum of life.

Flash forward to 2018

Back to my story, living at the retreat center after quitting my consulting job, Josh still wouldn't marry me and we fought constantly. I had been hired to help with sales at the retreat center, but I was failing. My savings were rapidly dwindling. I felt uneasy in my friendships, as if there were things we weren't saying to each other. Worst of all, I felt disconnected from myself, as if I couldn't quite hear my desires anymore. Without my desires, I felt devoid of guidance.

Needless to say, it was an emotional time for me. Every day I meditated and asked for guidance.

In April, I decided to join *Mama Gena's School of Womanly Arts*. My hope was that the six-month women's program would help me hear my inner voice more clearly and thereby know what to do next with my life.

In the second weekend of the program, Mama Gena told us we were going into our emotions. I was among four hundred women standing in a darkened auditorium, hushed and waiting, to learn how. *What would we do?!* I felt nervous, scared and intrigued.

She turned on the song *Killing in the Name* by *Rage Against the Machine* and began raging onstage. She punched pillows, screamed, kicked and tore apart her black bag of a dress. I stood shocked. I had never seen such a raw, primal display of anger before. It electrified me. The four hundred women in the auditorium were silent as we all watched her in awe.

Then she turned on *This Woman's Work* by *Kate Bush* and started grieving. She cried and wailed in deep primal sounds, throwing herself on the ground. It broke my heart to watch her like that. I felt uncomfortable, as if I wanted her to stop crying—just as my dad must have felt watching me as a three year old. But I was also transfixed. How could she be so free with her emotions?

Afterward, she danced to a sensual song, touching her body all over. The whole crowd of women joined in, moving our hips with hers. It felt like a reclamation.

Once complete, Mama Gena invited us to join in on this practice she called "Swamping." She announced she would play a song, and in pairs, one of us would rage while the other watched.

I felt skeptical. Feeling emotions on demand? Isn't that a bit artificial?

Once again, she put on *Killing in the Name* by *Rage Against the Machine* again and encouraged us to let our rage out. People around me were screaming and punching the air, and frankly, looked a bit possessed. I felt scared by this raw display of anger, but also...turned on by it.

And what did I have to lose? Not much. So I tried raging. At first, I felt as if I was being fake angry and playing a role. But slowly, real rage came out of me. I had no idea where the rage came from—it felt old, primal, deep. I screamed, surprising myself by the ferocity of my voice. *Whoa. Who is this woman?*

I felt such a relief afterward. I could breathe deeper. I was quite proud of myself. Who knew I was such a raging badass?!

Next, she played a grief song, *Giving Up Everything* by *Natalie Merchant* and encouraged us to feel our grief. To cry, to sway, to express. Again, I was skeptical. *Crying on demand? What am I, a damsel in distress?*

Women around me were wailing, sobbing, grieving as if they were in the middle of the most tragic heartbreak of their lives. I felt frozen. As Mama Gena encouraged the crowd, I began moving my body, swaying and shifting. I let my eyes close. Soon, I felt a little tender core in my heart that felt like genuine grief. I began to cry, softly at first and then loudly in big unselfconscious sobs. It was beautiful.

Afterward, I felt relaxed. What a relief to acknowledge my feelings, especially the ones buried deep inside that had no "reason" to be there. Moving our emotions with the other women also helped me feel connected.

Finally, Mama Gena invited us to bring turn on into our emotions by letting the emotions feel erotic and sexy. She flipped on*Artificial Red* by *Mad Season* as we all danced, touching our bodies, swaying our hips. As I danced my emotions through and touched my body, I felt, "Wow, not only are these emotions important...these emotions are also **sexy.**"

Emotions are energy-in-motion

Today I believe rage is sexy. Grief is sexy. Disgust is sexy. When we bring our sexiness or turn on into emotions, we find the power in our emotions.

From there, we can let our emotions inform our decisions and use the energy the emotions provide to fuel us. Emotions are energy-in-motion. They are meant to move through us and out of us in real time. If you've ever watched a baby, you know what pure emotions in motion look like. The baby cries, and then a second later the baby laughs, and a moment later the baby is angry, followed by laughter. Moment-to-moment emotional expression.

At our core, we're the same as that baby. Yet many of us have learned to clamp down on our emotions and then they get stuck in our bodies as tension and blockages.

What would it look like to reclaim the wisdom and the power of your emotions? To let every emotion move through you? To embrace the full keyboard of your feelings?

Over lunch, Mama Gena asked us to explore the question, "What would be possible in your life if you swamped consistently? What would change if you had access to your full emotions and knew you could move them through your body?"

I realized, "I'd be free. I wouldn't have to protect myself from pain, rage or grief. I could feel it all, move it and let it go. I would be more willing to take risks, to be bold and unafraid." It was a profound realization for me.

Let's explore four emotions in more depth—anger, grief, jealousy and shame. I notice many of my clients struggle with these four emotions, so below I provide the wisdom each holds and how to move through them.

Anger

*"Bitterness is like cancer. It eats upon the heart.
But anger is like fire. It burns it all clean."*
—Maya Angelou

Anger lets us know something important to us is in danger or has been violated.
Anger is our sign that something in our world is not quite right.
Anger gives us the fuel for action and for change.

Often when women start turning on and getting in touch with their desire, the first emotion that pops up is anger. Newer clients will say to me, "Megan, I don't understand. Suddenly I'm so angry at everything."

I cheer and applaud the women's anger. Why? Because anger is your desire saying, "Not this. I will not tolerate this. I know more is possible. Life can be more beautiful, more just than this."

Also, considering that she may have grown-up her entire life in a patriarchal system which devalues women...she may have a reason to be angry. Watching her mothers, her grandmothers and many generations of women before her devalued, discounted and oppressed may make a woman a wee bit angry.

So yes, many women are boiling with repressed anger. And rightly so.

Now she is presented with the question—what to do with this anger? How can she channel all this (justified) rage into a healthy direction?

> *Healthy anger is fuel for boundaries, action and transformation. The key is action. Anger is meant to be moved into action.*

Healthy anger is fuel for boundaries, action and transformation. The key is **action**. Anger is meant to be moved into action. For example, maybe you're angry at global warming, so you start a campaign to help save the oceans. Maybe you're angry at your ex, and that anger gives you the fuel to finally throw away all of her old stuff. Maybe you're angry at an injustice at work, and your rage gives you the courage to speak up to the leadership team.

Anger channeled into transformation is like a forest fire that rips through the trees, burning away the underbrush to clear space for new seeds to grow. It is important and necessary, even if it is a bit scary.

Without **action**, anger tends to fester. Old, repressed anger hardens into resentment and closed-heartedness.

Withheld anger can also turn inward as self-hatred and self-harm. Thoughts such as, "I can't believe I did that. I'm such an idiot," or, "Why am I such a coward?" are evidence of anger that's been held in and directed toward yourself. Many women are prone to this kind of inward-directed anger because we're taught that we're not allowed to have outward-directed anger.

> *Anger channeled into transformation is like a forest fire that rips through the trees, burning away the underbrush to clear space for new seeds to grow. It is important and necessary, even if it is a bit scary.*

Her anger sets her free

I recently coached a client who's partner came home with a DUI and a confession that he had been cheating on her. At first, she was numb and tried to rationally figure out what to do.

As this client connected with her anger, she began to stand up more firmly, with a straighter spine in her relationship. She was furious about the behaviors she had been tolerating. She told him no more cheating or he's out. When he cheated again, she left his stuff on the front porch. This time, for good.

Her refusal to tolerate this behavior led to him realizing he needed to change his life. He quit drinking and went to a twelve-step program. She moved on to find new partners who treat her better.

While this process was not easy, she discovered a sense of right-ness and dignity she'd forgotten many years before along with her repressed anger. By welcoming in her anger, she found courage to stand up for the treatment she deserved.

_____

What about you? What do you tend to do with your anger?

The swamping exercise at the end of this chapter is a great start next time you feel anger. It will help you embody and move this powerful emotion so the anger doesn't get stuck inside your body.

After you "swamp," I recommend taking a minute to reflect on:

- What is one **empowered action** I can take right now?
- How could I use this anger for change or to take a stand?
- What can I do to "right the wrongs" in this situation?

Grief

> "Someone needs to encourage us not to brush aside what we feel, not to be ashamed of the love and grief it arouses in us, not to be afraid of pain. Someone needs to encourage us that this soft spot in us could be awakened and that to do this would change our lives."
> —Pema Chodron, *When Things Fall Apart*

As I was struggling at the retreat center, I committed to meditating and asking Spirit every day, "Where do you want me now?"

While meditating, I began to see images of a tropical place, maybe Bali, leading women's retreats. These images felt so vivid, so real, it felt like seeing the future. These visions felt like remembering. Each time I saw this image of Bali, tears rolled down my cheeks and my arms covered in goosebumps.

Tears and goosebumps often alert me to something true, something deep and real. So I listened. I knew this was a message from my higher power.

A few days later, I sat down with Rev Jo, my spiritual mentor. She's an amazing elder—a Native American medicine woman, an art therapist, a minister at Agape, one of the only women in the world to know Aramaic. Basically, Rev Jo understands deep truth when she sees it.

I told her nothing felt right at the retreat center. My relationship with Josh was so rocky we could barely be in the same room together. I felt impotent, as if my efforts weren't making progress anywhere.

Then I told Rev Jo that every time I meditated, I saw images of leading women's retreats in Bali. As I told her, I began sobbing. Big, uncontrollable, gulping sobs. These sobs felt as if someone was dying, but I didn't know what it was.

Rev Jo told me, "Honey, Bali sounds like a calling on your life. I think you need to go."

I nodded silently. I knew she was right. But I also knew if I went to Bali, it would mean giving up everything I had created over the last five years. My tight-knit spiritual community. My relationship. My income with the retreat center. My identity as an *Orgasmic Meditation* teacher. It felt like a death to go to Bali.

After talking with Rev Jo, I had a morsel of courage, so I went back to my room and immediately bought a flight for a few days later. I didn't tell anyone right away, because I didn't want to be convinced not to go. I felt tenderly brave.

One by one, I said my goodbyes to my friends and the community. I explained, "I don't know exactly what I will do in Bali or why I'm going. It's just a feeling."

Once safely on the plane, I began openly crying. I looked through the photos on my phone, saying goodbye to all these people I loved so dearly. I grieved as if someone was dying. And it was—the identity and life I had created, the "me" I used to be was all dying.

I knew Bali would be an exciting new adventure, but first I needed to honor my sadness and what I was leaving behind.

I almost always cry on the plane, as flying represents leaving someone or something. I used to worry what the people around me would think of me, this sad girl flying alone with tears streaming down her face. But now, I tell myself—my tears have a place. My tears represent transition. Letting go of the old to make space for the new life I have yet to live.

Tears create space

Tears are the way our body cleanses stuckness to create a wide open space inside of us. Our grief is a way to honor that which we have loved and released.

When we deny our grief, we get stuck in the past. We can't move forward. We hold on to old grudges. We obsessively wonder, "What if?"

Our grief is the fuel to help us move forward. Grief softens our hearts and opens our capacity for compassion. As we stay steady with our own pain, we grow our capacity to be with others in their pain. In this way, it is a sacred act to grieve, as it makes space for more love in our lives.

Sometimes there is a clear reason to grieve, as when something tangible in the outside world is lost. Example: someone dies, a relationship ends, your dog gets sick, a friend hurts your feelings, etc. There is a "reason" to cry.

Other times, grief will come up seemingly out of nowhere. You may feel blue, and an hour later, you're crying on the phone with a friend without knowing why. You wake up with a heavy heart, and lie in bed wondering what happened. You say goodbye to your sister and tears form even though you'll see her next week.

This is what I call "everyday ordinary grief." I believe this is the grief of recognizing that everything in our world is impermanent. Moments when we realize (consciously or unconsciously) that the plants we love today will wilt, our favorite pets will die, our relationships will end, this talk with our sister is coming to a close, or this kiss is over.

Everyday ordinary grief is how we honor all of the thousands of tiny deaths we face every day in every little way. When we make space to feel everyday ordinary grief, we honor the transient nature of beauty and the love in our life. We exhale. We surrender and let go.

The USA culture in which I grew up is hell-bent on finding joy and excitement, while also denying grieving. That is like taking a sharp inhale without any exhale. No wonder we Americans are so puffed-up, anxious and stressed! Grieving gives us a deep exhalation, the letting go so many of us crave.

Our grief has a timeline of its own. Grief is meant to move through our bodies at its own pace and its own rhythm. I used to fear that if I let myself go into grief, I'd get stuck forever and never find my way back to joy.

That hasn't been my experience at all. Instead, when I let myself go into grief, I feel a deep relaxation, and then a spontaneous joy usually emerges at the end of the grieving.

Embracing the reality of everyday ordinary grief turns your sadness from a "problem to solve" into a beautiful, heart-opening experience to relish. It reframes what's happening inside of you from something "bad" into a chance to honor what you love.

Do you have trouble accessing your grief? I did, too, for many years. In fact, I didn't cry once for two whole years! Now, I cry a few times a week, which I believe is a great sign of cleansing. If, like me, you've struggled to access your grief after years of repressing it, the *Grief Cocoon* exercise at the end of this chapter will help.

Stuck in grief? If you have let yourself fully feel your grief and the grief still feels stuck, as if you can't move through it, then this may be a good time to hire a great therapist, coach or psychiatrist to help you. Stuck grief may be your body, calling for a little extra support and love. Goodness knows, I have benefitted enormously from external help myself.

Jealousy

After my tear-filled plane ride, I arrived in Bali feeling utterly alone.

As I unpacked my clothes and laid out my little altar, I realized this was the first time I'd had my own room in five years. While part of the *Orgasmic Meditation* community, I'd always shared a room and I had gotten used to the bustling noise of group living. Now all around me was quiet. Stillness.

A part of me loved the stillness. Inside of it, I discovered my own rhythms. What time do I like to wake up? Go to bed? What morning practice feels best to me? How do I like to structure my days? It felt spacious and tender to be alone, getting to know myself like this.

My sense of solo peace was abruptly shattered one day when I received a text from my friend Marissa. She said she'd been sleeping with Josh, my ex of only one week ago, and that she was beginning to have feelings for him. She admitted she may want to explore more emotional intimacy with him, perhaps even a relationship.

My chest caved in and I felt punched in my stomach. I immediately burst into tears.

While a part of me was happy for her because I knew she'd wanted a boyfriend for a long time, another (bigger) part of me was devastated. It was confusing, weirdly intimate and deeply painful.

I asked to know more. She shared about their sex, what it was like, how tender she felt with him.

That text was like a kick in the gut. Even though I had asked for it, I wasn't prepared to receive that much information. Jealousy, that green-eyed monster, threatened to overtake me.

Luckily, I had been training to handle this emotion. I had spent years in open relationships, cultivating my capacity to be with the intensity of jealousy.

I focused on the physical sensations in my body.
My pounding heart.
My fluttery belly.
My watery eyes.
My tight throat.

As I noticed these sensations, I deliberately kept my attention in my body and out of stories.

Marissa asked me, "Is this okay? Would you rather I stop seeing him? I will if you want me to. Our friendship matters more to me."

Truthfully, I didn't want her to stop seeing him. In a weird way, hearing about them being together gave me a sense of closure. I knew I didn't want him back, and their dating definitely closed that door. Still, though, it was immensely painful.

"No," I said. "It hurts, but it is okay. I'm happy for you."

I tucked my phone away and closed my eyes. I held my hand over my heart and whispered to myself, "I am safe. I am loved." I wrapped my arms around myself, letting myself feel all the feels. I soothed myself as I let the tears come like a dark storm passing through.

In that moment, I felt my jealousy, yes, but I also felt my vulnerability, my tenderness, my incredible strength and our sisterhood. All of it mixed up into one potent moment.

Jealousy is a complex emotion. It's not as straightforward as feeling insecure, as some polyamorists will tell you, nor is it as simple as envy.

Jealousy is the experience of coming face-to-face with our own electric vulnerability. Of loving someone, yet seeing how totally powerless we are to keep that person all to ourselves.

> *Jealousy is the experience of coming face-to-face with our own electric vulnerability. Of loving someone, yet seeing how totally powerless we are to keep that person all to ourselves.*

Jealousy reminds us that no connection is permanent and no relationship is entirely secure. The wisdom of jealousy lies in this uncertainty—it shocks us out of our comfort zones and brings us to our vulnerabilities. Jealousy is like 1000 volts of electricity waking us back up to our tender hearts.

I have felt jealous many times in my life. From the outside, I appear to be a secure and steady human but I can become incredibly insecure, jealous and possessive. In order to befriend this green-eyed monster, I have chosen all kinds of different relationship arrangements, including polyamory. These experiences taught me so much about working with my nervous system and my psyche while jealous.

Here are the three biggest tips I've learned about working with jealousy.

1. **Make no sudden moves.** When jealousy strikes, our rational brain goes offline and our survival brain kicks in. We may want to do something impulsive such as slash his tires, scream or block our ex on all social media accounts. Resist the urge to do anything immediately. Just breathe. Be with yourself. Pause.

2. **Name the physical sensations** in your body. Tight throat, hard belly, electric pussy, tense heart, etc. Naming sensations keeps you rooted in your body and in this moment rather than spinning off into fear-based thoughts.

3. **Find ways to comfort yourself** and soothe your nervous system. Touch your body. Take a salt bath. Ask a friend for a hug. Whisper affirmations. Pray. Meditate. Whatever helps you slow your breathing down and feel connected to something bigger than yourself will be useful here.

Jealousy is an unavoidable experience, a core part of being human.

In relationships, many people try to avoid getting jealous by setting up strict monogamy rules for their relationship and punishing their partner when they break the "rules." This is not a great long-term strategy as it leads to a narrow, constricted, conditional form of love, and usually, jealousy eventually arrives anyway. Rather than trying to avoid jealousy entirely, see if you can befriend the discomfort and intensity of it.

Jealousy is not confined to romantic relationships. You can get jealous of many things—your friends' business success, your sister's fashion sense, your cousin's new baby. In all these places, jealousy is like smoke on the fire of your desire. Feeling jealous simply means, "I want what you have." (More on this in Chapter 16 in regard to sisterhood.)

In all cases, can you befriend your own jealousy? Get intimate with the tenderness of your vulnerability? Maybe even find play inside your jealousy? If you can be with the 1000 volts of electricity that is jealousy, you will become less afraid and more generous with your love.

Shame

Shame makes our shoulders roll in, makes us hide our faces, and closes our hearts. It is the only emotion I don't believe holds any wisdom.

Shame is a learned emotion based on social conditioning. We are not born ashamed of who we are. Shame is something that creeps up on us from all these little insidious messages from culture, family, the media, etc. that tells us we're not good enough, we'll never be good enough, we haven't done enough, we haven't earned our right to exist on Earth.

Shame is not an intrinsic part of being a human. Shame is passed down generation to generation to generation. Shame can be healed, layer by layer, in the presence of loving, nonjudgmental support.

Let me tell you a story. A few years prior to moving to Bali, I was in my coaching program, learning how to become a life coach. One weekend, we explored intimacy, and specifically, the unique ways we block intimacy. In a crowd of 150 people, I sat journaling about my past relationships guided by the facilitator on stage.

In this work, I discovered something about myself that disgusted me—that I often block intimacy by trying to be superior to other people. I was horrified to see the truth of my own elitism, written down, with evidence from my past relationships. I felt repulsed by that behavior. I couldn't believe I would do that. What kind of selfish egomaniac tries to be better than others?!

Ashamed, I quickly covered up my paper so no one next to me could see what I had written.

Next, the facilitator said, "Now you are going to stand up, find a partner and read what you wrote down to your partner."

I froze. Oh God, no. I wanted to die. My cheeks burned and my armpits began to sweat. I didn't want to read this to someone else. My friend Amber asked to be my partner. "Uhhh...sure," I muttered.

She looked at me with her big brown eyes, waiting for me to share.

I managed to read to her what was on my paper with my eyes cast down. As I read, tears slid down my cheeks. I felt so ashamed.

When I looked up, she was staring back at me with her eyes full of love and understanding. She wasn't judging me. She got it. And she still loved me. She said, "Me too. I act superior sometimes, too, when I'm scared."

I cried harder. As I cried, I felt as if those tears were cleansing the shame off me. Maybe I didn't have to be so ashamed that I sometimes act superior. Maybe a lot of people do that. Maybe it's just part of our protective mechanisms.

In that moment, my shame dissipated.

That's how shame disappears—person to person, with compassionate, loving listening.

Do you feel ashamed?

Shame can be a sneaky emotion. At that time, I wouldn't have said I experienced shame. I was popular, successful and beautiful. What was there to be ashamed of?

But as I discovered, shame is often found in the shadow of the "rules" we hold for ourselves. Rules such as, "Don't cry in public," or, "Be successful," or, "Act chill and nonchalant," or, "Look good." Shame threatens us in the background—"Follow these rules or you won't be loved." Shame is the thick rope that binds us to "behave."

So if you feel tight, tense or controlling...shame may be the secret culprit.

The best way to clear shame is to share your secrets with someone who feels safe. Practice revealing your inner world to that person in small doses. In their continued love, you will begin to see that you are worthy of love.

Shame is essentially a social construct, built person to person. To heal shame, you must rewrite that story person to person. You cannot read a book, take a course, or journal your way out of shame. As far as I can tell, the only way out of shame is by admitting your secrets to another human being and seeing you are still loved.

To this end, if you are struggling with shame, I highly recommend twelve-step programs. I believe the root of all addictions and controlling compulsions is socially learned shame. Twelve-step programs help you identify the root of your shame, share it in a safe space and heal. There are twelve-step programs for every kind of addiction all over the world. Codependents Anonymous is the program I've worked with for years, which is a great general twelve-step program. The only requirement for membership is a desire for healthy and loving relationships. A simple Google search should help you find a twelve-step program near you or a group that meets online.

The Courage Not to Numb

Lastly, it is an incredibly brave decision to let yourself be a full spectrum woman who feels it all. Most women do not.

We learn early on expressing intense emotions will cause us to be perceived as crazy, hysterical or unstable. As a result, many women repress their feelings, pushing them down. Then we wonder why we can't feel anything at all.

How do we numb our emotions? In a thousand ways. Here's a few common ones:

- Overeating or overindulging
- Using drugs and alcohol
- Shopping, excessive spending, gambling
- Overanalyzing / stuck in our heads
- Trying to control other people's actions (to avoid our own feelings)
- Avoiding uncomfortable situations such as conflict
- Staying overly busy

- Caretaking others (rather than caring for ourselves)
- Overachieving and endless striving
- Too much time on social media
- Binge-watching TV

Can you relate to any of these?

If so, it's okay! Most of us numb ourselves in one way or another. Sometimes we just aren't ready to feel our emotions. The emotions may feel too overwhelming, scary or difficult to process.

Do your best not to feel shame about numbing. It's normal. Just notice yourself doing it with gentle awareness, and then, if you can, choose another behavior.

For years, I numbed my emotions through overwork, people pleasing, alcohol and staying overly busy. Then I wondered why I hadn't cried in two years, and didn't feel much pleasure, either. (The extent to which we repress the darkness is the extent to which we deny the light.)

When I finally became aware of my own numbness, I was frustrated. I wanted to feel my feelings! But my emotions didn't come right away. One of the best pieces of advice I ever got was, "Move gradually and gently into emotions, giving yourself lots of space and permission. Your emotional world is like a lake full of fish with a frozen top layer. Gradually, with practice, you will melt the frozen top layer and get to know the fish of your emotions again."

She was right! With patience and practice, I began to "thaw" and feel my feelings again. Now I have a rich, vivid emotional world.

Feeling numb? The below exercises will help you to slowly discover your emotional world, as well.

Exercise: Swamping

This is the exercise I did in Mama Gena's mastery program. It is incredibly powerful, especially when done with other women.

You can access my personal playlist for Swamping on my website: **www.megandlambert.com/book**.

Instructions

1. Create a safe space where you won't be disturbed. If you're doing this with girlfriends, choose one person to witness and one person to express. The witness watches the other person, beaming love and approval.

2. Find a rage song.

3. If you're the person expressing, begin moving rage through your body. You may try punching the air, screaming into a pillow or scrunching up your face in an angry expression. At first it may feel fake, as if you're putting on an act. That's okay. Keep going.

4. Allow the emotion to fully express itself.

5. Then, put on a sad song.

6. Let yourself grieve. Feel your heart, sway your body. Again, it's okay if it feels fake at first. Eventually you may touch on genuine sadness.

7. Lastly, put on a sexy song that turns on your body.

8. Move your body in sensual, sexy ways. Let yourself be turned on by your own damned body. Bringing eroticism into our "dark" emotions helps us reclaim the power in those emotions instead of feeling victimized by them.

9. Enjoy! If you're with another person, go ahead and switch roles now so you are now witnessing them.

If you'd like, you may choose to share a favorite moment with each other afterward to help integrate the exercise.

10. Notice how you feel after Swamping. More open? Relief? An exhale? What would be possible if you regularly swamped your emotions?

11. Feel free to continue exploring other emotional flavors through music and movement if you'd like, such as disgust, surprise, innocence, fear, shame and love.

Exercise: Grief Cocoon

If you have a hard time feeling grief, as I did for many years, I'd recommend creating a container for your grief. Like a caterpillar crawling into a cocoon to transform, this exercise gives you a "safe space" to explore the novel terrain of your own grief.

Instructions

1. Set aside at least ten minutes where you won't be disturbed.

2. Close the doors and the curtains. Create a private, dark, uninterrupted space for yourself. You can even curl up under the covers of your bed. This creates a cocoon of safety to let yourself go into unknown emotional spaces.

3. Set a timer for 10 minutes, then line up a few sad songs and pop in your ear buds. I personally like *Paralyzed* by **NF**, *Let It Go* by **James Bay**, and *Hallelujah* by **Jeff Buckley**.

4. Next, close your eyes and feel your heart. Notice if there's any tightness or holding. Breathe it open.

5. It may help to imagine a sad scenario in your life right now. You can also imagine a sad scenario globally such as global warming, mass extinctions, etc.

6. Continue breathing and feeling. You may move your body in circles, rolling out your head and neck and shoulders.

7. Let yourself cry or make sounds if you want. Allow your body to express itself. If no tears come, let that be okay, too.

8. When the timer goes off, dry your eyes, place a hand on your heart and thank yourself for your courage to feel. It is a brave, rebellious action. Remind yourself that whatever you felt, even if it wasn't much, is perfect.

During this exercise, you may feel nothing. That's okay, too. The more space you create in your life for emotion, the more emotion will begin to flow freely, and the more open your heart will feel. Give yourself time, slowly, slowly.

Invitation: Grab Your Journal

1. What did you learn growing up about "dark" emotions such as rage, grief, jealousy and shame? Did you feel safe to express those emotions?

2. How do you treat these emotions today? As an inconvenience, as an embarrassment, as a gift, as guidance?

3. What would it look like to embrace the full spectrum of your emotions? What might become possible for you?

4. If you're feeling an intense emotion right now, what might that emotion be telling you? What wisdom may be hidden there? Try not to analyze the emotion with your mind; rather, feel with your gut for an intuitive answer.

CHAPTER 10

CELEBRATING OUR CYCLES

We have all of nature inside of us. With our emotions, we discover different "weather patterns" as well as the wisdom and joy in each emotional weather. Next, with our menstrual cycle, we understand our "seasons." Just as nature moves through winter, spring, summer and fall, so too do we move through these seasons with the weeks of our cycles.

Understanding the cyclical nature of the feminine body is life-changing information. It can teach us to live in a more rhythmic, sustainable and intuitive way.

If you do not menstruate, this chapter is still for you! Consider using the moon cycle as a guide to cyclical living (more information below). Whether you menstruate or not, this chapter will give you the tools and perspective to be more connected to your own cyclical nature.

Discovering My Own Rhythm

By this time, I had decided I wanted to live in Bali full-time. I began looking for a home and found a cute little one bedroom place to rent with a tiny pool and yard. My first solo house! I loved decorating the space with my drawings and paintings.

I also began my coaching business in earnest. I had a big vision to help hundreds of people find more love, better sex and clearer inner harmony. After five years of studying desire and cultivating my coaching skills, I was eager to share what I knew with the world.

While the overachiever in me would happily work for ten hours a day, I began to notice some weeks I could sustain that rate, while other weeks I would need more rest and maybe even a nap (gasp!). I began tracking my energy and realized the pattern was cyclical. It exactly followed my menstrual cycle.

Fascinated, I read books around the menstrual cycle and began talking to other women about their cycles. There was a definite rhythm which I'd never noticed or been taught. It felt like discovering a secret feminine language. Now that I was becoming aware of these cycles, my entire life was changing.

By using the wisdom of my cycles, I didn't need to push or force myself anymore. I realized there is a time each month when I am naturally high energy, focused and extroverted; while at other times, I am naturally more reflective, thoughtful and full of visions. When I followed my own energy patterns, I felt more relaxed and in flow.

I began planning my business around my menstrual cycle. When I was ovulating, I would organize speaking events and podcast interviews, launch programs and lead workshops. When I was menstruating, I would rest and reflect on the month. While in my follicular phase (before ovulation), I would set new intentions, desires and hopes. While in my luteal phase (post ovulation), I would complete projects, tie up loose ends and eliminate unnecessary tasks. Of course, my work schedule wasn't always this tidy, but even shifting just 20% of my work to follow my menstrual cycle had a profound impact on me.

This meant while I deeply loved my work, I didn't feel drained by it. Instead, as I trusted my body to guide me, I felt enlivened and inspired by my work each week. I also discovered a whole new level of self-acceptance and self-love by acknowledging the brilliance of my natural cycles.

Reclaiming Our Wild Nature Through Menstrual Cycles

This section is about RECLAIMING our wild, natural feminine ways. We can't truly do that unless we embrace our inherent cyclical nature. Unless we realize that, just like nature's seasons and the moon's cycles, we, too, undergo seasons and cycles. We must realize we are not the machines or robots we may try to be—that in fact, we are more primal, more animal and more natural than that.

Our menstrual cycles give us a clear roadmap on how to connect back in with our wild, natural feminine.

Many of us grew up in a world obsessed with sterilization, disinfectant and tidy edges. We are taught to be neat, pulled together, smell lovely and appear polished. We try to be consistent and persistent, just like a machine.

Yet, we have this wild, wet, messy side of us, too. For many of us, this part of us lives in the shadows, repressed and denied. Our menstruation invites us back into the wild, the mess, the lush saturation of what it means to be a female. This is a chance to remember not only is it okay to be messy, but that messy is our birthplace.

Consider childbirth. It includes blood, tears, sometimes poop, sweat, moans and groans and eventually a crying baby. In a way, childbirth is all "mess." Yet can you deny that a baby's birth is one of the most beautiful, meaningful moments in a person's life? That's the power of the feminine. We are not meant to be bone dry, sterile and pristine. We're meant to be flushed, saturated, moist and fully alive.

What comes to mind when you hear the word "messy" or "moist?"

Cosmopolitan magazine recently published an article on women's most hated words. Guess what was #1? Moist.

I believe that is because we're taught to push away anything that makes us untamed and feminine, especially our own body's fluids (unless we are pressured to "get wet" for a man's pleasure). This chapter is about questioning that script. It will introduce you to the profound beauty of your cyclical nature.

My First Period

I was thirteen years old when suddenly I noticed a brownish spot on my underwear. I got scared, thinking I had an infection, because I assumed periods were always red. Crying, I called my step-mom, afraid I would have to have a doctor poke and prod me in my most intimate spot because there was something wrong with me.

She reassured me and said, "Maybe you just started your period?" She brought home pads and told me to go tell my dad. Even though I grew up in a household that openly talked about puberty, I still felt ashamed and wanted to hide.

Somehow I knew that to get my period in today's culture was not a sacred or special milestone—it was shameful, something to be hidden away, ignored and rarely discussed.

Can you relate?

Many of us grow up with overt or covert messages that our periods are dirty, gross and unclean. We try to hide it with weird scented tampons, "no-show" pads and dark jeans. We hope no one notices.

In many religious sites such as some temples or churches, women aren't even allowed inside while we're bleeding because we are "unclean."

How did our female cycles, the very birthplace of humanity, become so degraded and disgraced?

It Wasn't Always Like This

There was a time, thousands of years ago, when a woman's first bleed was a sacred milestone. Her first bleed marked her entrance into womanhood, and the whole tribe would celebrate her with sweets, songs, flowers and more. Bleeding for the first time was something to which she could look forward and of which she could feel proud. Often, she would collect her blood and pour it onto the earth as a sacred offering for mother nature.

When women would bleed together, they would gather in "red tents," a place of celebration where they could rest and support each other. In Native American traditions, it was said that menstruating women would sleep with their heads together in a circle so they could dream for the tribe. While they slept, they would receive intuitive insights about where the tribe should go next and other mystical messages. The community relied on this "bleeding" wisdom for guidance and direction.

Can you imagine?

Can you imagine a world where your first bleed was honored and celebrated? Where you felt no shame, only pride and joy, at the spotting on your underpants? Where your feminine cycle was honored as the birthplace of all humanity, a sign of your fertility and womanhood? Where your bleeding wisdom was honored and revered?

I hope my daughters are born into a world like that. This book and these teachings are for our daughters, so they can live in a world that is kind and reverent toward the sacred feminine within them.

Why Is This Important Now?

When we are connected to our menstrual cycles, we restore balance and flow within our bodies. By honoring our cycle, we also honor and connect with nature and Mother Earth. We release the neverending weight of the world (and our to-do lists) and allow our natural feminine rhythm of nourish-create-nourish-create.

We are made to spend part of our time inward on nourishing, resting, and restoring ourselves; as well as part of our time outward on connecting, creating and nurturing others. Understanding and following our cycles help us balance these two impulses—the giving and the receiving.

Often the modern woman is deeply imbalanced. She's been giving, giving, giving and doing, doing, doing. She wants to "keep up" with men, so she tries to be in eternal summer, tries to sustain the natural high energy of her ovulation phase.

Unfortunately, by chasing an "eternal summer" of constant production, extroversion and high energy, she denies the other vital, life-giving three phases of her cycle. Without the other three phases, she will quickly become depleted. The rise of adrenal fatigue, burnout and exhaustion in modern women shows the stress of this.

When the modern woman pushes and pushes, denying her need for the entire cyclical process, including rest and reflection, her weary body and tense mind show the result. Have you been this woman, trying to hold the world on her shoulders? I know I have.

When we honor our cycles, we feel more at peace with ourselves. No longer fighting our bodies or pushing ourselves to perform, we can relax into the ancient knowing that this too shall pass and that everything happens in the right time. We give ourselves permission to rest and restore, which in turn makes our productive phase all the more productive.

> *When we honor our cycles, we feel more at peace with ourselves. No longer fighting our bodies or pushing ourselves to perform, we can relax into the ancient knowing that this too shall pass and that everything happens in the right time. We give ourselves permission to rest and restore, which in turn makes our productive phase all the more productive.*

If we can celebrate each of the four phases of our menstrual cycle, we feel more free to express the different archetypes inside us, resulting in less restriction and limitation. In that freedom, we feel more self-acceptance, self-love and inner harmony.

I know that sounds like a big promise from understanding your menstrual cycle.

Yet, this has certainly been the case for me and for the women with whom I work. I invite you to read on with an open mind and consider how this information may be useful for you, too.

Cyclical Time vs. Linear Time

The way we track time has a profound impact on how we choose to live our lives. Why? Because many people see time as the ultimate scarce resource. We can always make more money, but despite our best efforts toward immortality, our days on earth are finite.

Culturally, we tend to think of time linearly, counting hours, months and years,as one steady progression from birth to death. We treat time like a roll of toilet paper—steadily running out. This linear view is just one way to view time—a more masculine approach.

When we view time from this masculine, linear angle, we often feel as if there is never enough time. The to-do list is long and endless. We can't get everything done. The clock is our enemy, slowly counting down our hours on earth. This viewpoint makes us push ourselves to do more and be more, to "carpe diem" or seize the day—all day, every day. Yet this wreaks havoc on our bodies.

There is another way. Again, we can learn about ourselves by studying nature. Nature works cyclically, in seasons. Some months are for planting, for growing, for harvesting, for resting. Viewing time cyclically is more like a wheel rolling forward, constantly regenerating itself.

Our feminine bodies are made to run on cyclical time. How? Our menstrual (or moon) cycles give us the roadmap for how to view time as a circle, constantly changing and regenerating just like our bodies. By moving cyclically, we feel more connected to nature, ourselves and the wider life cycles.

The Four Women Inside

Throughout our menstrual cycle, we move through four different "seasons" of womanhood. These seasons bring out different archetypes, or ways of being, inside of us. By welcoming these different archetypes, we can discover the wisdom that each one has to offer us.

I recommend using my descriptions below as a general guideline, yet also track your own cycle and observe your unique rhythm. There are many apps you can use for this—Kindara and MyFlo are my current favorites.

Side Note: Not Menstruating or on Birth Control?

If you're on hormonal birth control (the pill, hormonal IUD, shot, patch, etc.), then your body is in "pseudopregnancy" from the artificial hormones. This means you don't undergo a typical menstrual cycle. You may still bleed when you stop taking the pills for a few days, but because you haven't ovulated, your body will not have the same hormone shifts.

Alternatively, you may be past menopause, or yet to begin your cycle, or you may identify as a woman but not have menstrual cycles. In any case, you can still live cyclically without a menstrual cycle.

How?

You can track and follow the cycles of the moon. A woman's typical menstrual cycle is around 28-32 days, and the moon's cycle is 29.5 days. Coincidence? I think not. We're more connected to the rhythms of the earth than our current culture would have us believe.

Below, I outline how the moon cycle symbolically aligns with the menstrual cycle. Feel free to use either or both cycles as a way to understand time from a cyclical angle.

Personally, I like to track both my menstrual cycle to understand my inner rhythm and the moon cycle to keep a pulse on the collective rhythm. I also find it interesting to notice when my menstrual cycle aligns with the moon cycle (traditionally, that means bleeding during the new moon) and when it doesn't.

As with anything, self-observation takes priority over intellectual knowledge. Your body may be similar to what I've written below, or you may notice differences—either is great. If your cycle feels very off or problematic, please do seek professional advice, ideally from a holistic wellness practitioner.

With that said, let's get to know the four women inside of us!

Spring (Follicular Phase) - Maiden - Waxing Moon

Imagine a young woman walking peacefully and happily down a garden lane. She's wearing a flowing white dress, surrounded by fresh new spring flowers and sunshine, with birds singing in the air. She bends down to plant a few seeds in the earth, eager to watch her newly planted seeds bloom.

Idyllic, right?

This is your inner "springtime," represented by the Maiden archetype. Just after you finish bleeding, you move into the follicular phase. If you're tracking by the moon, the springtime would be the waxing moon, when the moon gradually grows in size.

This is a time for fresh ideas, new inspiration, new creative projects. You may want to try something new, such as a new workout routine or a new way to work. The air feels light and open, full of possibilities.

Internally, you may feel youthful and innocent like the maiden, with an eagerness to explore and socialize. You may have a bright, budding desire for sexuality and enjoy flirting. You'll likely feel an increase in energy, and like the waxing moon, a growing desire to be seen.

Springtime is the time to plant new creative seeds. What do you want to experience during the next twenty-eight ish days (days will vary woman to woman)? What new projects would you like to begin? What ideas are drawing your attention?

Summer (Ovulation) - The Mother - The Full Moon

Picture a rowdy beach barbecue. The music is bumping, the drinks are flowing and laughter surrounds you. You're with your closest friends, celebrating the height of summer, joyful and exuberant. You run to take a swim in the ocean and cheer as the cold water hits your skin. Moments later, your love interest joins you in the water, and you two share a passionate kiss. Your whole body is buzzing with electricity, aliveness and excitement. This is the flavor of summer, representing ovulation and the full moon.

Following spring, your body moves into "summer" season, which is ovulation, where you are also the most fertile. If you're tracking by the moon, this is the five or so days surrounding the full moon.

Summer is all about being noticed, connecting and nurturing. You likely feel full of energy and confidence, as if you could take on the world. This week is associated with the "Mother" archetype, as you may notice that you feel particularly generous with your love and affection. You likely have extra attention to put on your loved ones.

In business, summer is the time to focus on sales, networking and launching new products. I always line up my program launches with the full moon or my ovulation, as I know I tend to be more high energy and confident during this time.

Biology is smart. During "summer," your sex drive is at an all-time high, and you may feel the urge to kiss and cuddle with your lover(s), which makes sense, given that your body is most fertile this week. If you're dating, studies show you will be drawn toward more dominant, assertive partners in power positions this week. You're physically the most attractive this week, with the best facial symmetry, so it's a great time to celebrate your beauty.

Foodwise, this is the time to eat healthy, vibrant foods including salads, fresh fruits and vegetables and light grains. Your body probably feels strong and energetic and you may be drawn to more high-intensity workouts such as HIIT or running.

Full Moon

A few special notes on the full moon, as this is an important time collectively as well as individually. The full moon is a time of celebration, community gatherings, and completion. Many religious holidays (such as Easter) are based around the full moon.

Many people struggle to sleep during the full moon because of an increase in energy. Hospitals staff more workers because there are more crimes and accidents during a full moon. Teachers report that children become more rowdy during this time. Generally, the intensity, energy, and enthusiasm rises as the moon becomes more visible (see, we're not that different from wolves ;)).

Fall (Luteal Phase) - The Wild Woman - Waning Moon

Picture walking down an autumn lane. The air is crisp against your skin so you pull your scarf in close. Multi-hued leaves gently drift down from the trees and crackle under your feet. You walk with a few friends, engaged in a deep conversation. When your friend asks your opinion on her new love interest, you share it honestly and insightfully. Feeling fatigued, you wander home to have a cup of tea by the fire and complete your project.

Sharp. Crackling. Deep. Slowing down.

Autumn begins after ovulation/full moon, as your body moves into the luteal phase of your cycle and the moon begins to wane.

This is a time for winding projects down, completing loose ends, finalizing structures and systems. You may feel more inward and reflective than the week before, making this an ideal time to sit down and focus on the task at hand.

In the early fall phase, you may still feel high energy, social, and productive—lingering impacts from summer. As time wears on, you likely will begin to feel more inward, quiet and reflective. Just as the moon gradually hides herself from our view, we too may feel the impulse to gently tuck away from the external world.

Romantically, you may not feel as bright and turned on as the week prior. You likely need more foreplay and softer touch to feel turned on. You may crave slow, relaxed lovemaking.

If you feel irritated by everyone, take this as a sign that your body is asking for more alone time, and honor it. Often this phase requires us to dial down the socializing and outward generosity and to bring more of our attention toward ourselves.

In terms of food, you may crave more earthy foods including pumpkin, kale, root vegetables, barley and quinoa. These types of earthy vegetables and grains will help nourish and sustain you. You may feel inclined toward "homemaking" activities this week— decorating, baking and nesting.

As your levels of progesterone rise, you'll likely feel more tired and sleepy than the two week's prior. This is normal—if you can, give yourself permission to move slower and take naps.

Often, if we don't honor our bodies' need for more rest, slowness and solitude during this time, we will become irritable and emotional. Doctors call this PMS (premenstrual syndrome) as if it is a disease, but the way I see it, irritability is our body asking for us to slow down and listen.

This period of time is named after the Wild Woman, as our emotions may become louder, our opinions may become stronger and our voices may become sharper. Any pain we haven't expressed often rises to the surface. We may angrily realize we haven't said certain truths. Or we may cry more freely, discovering hurts we didn't grieve. This is a powerful time to clear out any emotional charge that's built up from the month prior. It's a chance to say all the unsaid things and admit changes we need to make in our lives.

Like the Wild Woman, our intuition is sharp this week. Anything that's not quite in alignment will become very loud. You are not crazy. If you're feeling extra emotional or extra irritable, then pay attention, slow down, journal and listen to what your body is trying to tell you.

This is also a time for letting go. Clear out your closets, get rid of old things, eliminate draining habits and say goodbye to toxic relationships. During this phase, we begin releasing what we no longer need in order to create space for our new intentions and hopes.

Winter (Menstruation) - The Crone - The New Moon

See yourself curled up in a soft, fluffy bed. Snow gently falls outside your window. You're tucked away from the world, safe and warm under the covers with a mug of rich hot chocolate. You drift in and out of sleep, dreaming vividly about unseen worlds. Nothing to do and nowhere to go, you let out a big sigh of relief. Ahhh... With that exhale, you let go completely and relax into your cocoon to restore. Peaceful, right?

That's the flavor of winter, which is when you begin to bleed. If you're following the moon cycle, winter is roughly five days around the new moon.

Winter is the most underappreciated—yet deeply profound—time of our cycle. This is the time where you are most "yin," or inward and receptive, during your whole cycle. You likely need a little extra gentleness, caretaking and love during this phase, from yourself and/or a loved one.

In ancient times, women would excuse themselves from their daily responsibilities and retreat to a "red tent" while they were bleeding. This gave them time to rest and dream, without the burden of obligation (for more on this, I recommend the book "The Red Tent" by Anita Diamant).

While bleeding, the mystics say that the veil between this life and the world of spirits or the supernatural is the thinnest. This means while you bleed, especially during the first three days, you may receive psychic insights or intuitive understandings. Meditating, resting and praying are powerful activities that can give you inner clarity during this time.

This is a time of letting go physically and emotionally. For this reason, winter time can be draining on your body. You may find yourself craving seaweed, red meat or all kinds of interesting foods when you're bleeding. In general, I recommend trusting your body's cravings when it comes to food. Often, these cravings may indicate a missing nutrient your body needs to restore itself. In terms of fitness, if you feel up for it, gentle yoga, walking or soft exercise works best.

When it comes to sex in wintertime, every woman is diffferent. Some women feel extra sexual when they're bleeding, while other women don't want to be touched. Trust your desires here. Typically, your body will be very sensitive, so you may prefer slow, connected, gentle sex.

You likely need extra rest and restoration during this time—and may feel scratchy or irritable if you don't get it. Letting your intimate partner know that you'll be sensitive and raw during this time can save you many fights. Ask for extra compassion and gentleness.

"Winter" is a great time to reflect on the previous cycle and observe patterns. I'm from Silicon Valley, where start-up companies famously conduct "post-mortems" after major projects. "Post-mortem" literally means "after death." In this context, it is a way to reflect after completing a big project on what went well and what was learned.

The new moon, or your "inner winter," is the perfect opportunity for a "post-mortem" of your previous menstrual cycle. Questions to reflect on:

- What did you learn during the last twenty-nine(ish) days?
- What went well?
- What do you now know that you didn't before?
- What new wisdom have you gained this cycle?

In addition to a "post-mortem" review, if I feel up for it, I also like to host a "New Moon Ritual." While my full moon celebrations tend to be energetic, loud and social, my new moon rituals are more mysterious, private and mystical.

Here are a few ideas on how you can celebrate the new moon:

- Host a witchy ritual with crystals and tarot cards
- Write down and burn what you're releasing
- Have a heart-to-heart with a girlfriend
- Journal on your intentions for the next cycle
- Do a slow, sensual dance, either solo or with a partner

Summary

Tracking and aligning your actions with the moon and/or your menstrual cycle may help you feel more centered, grounded and refreshed each month. This process honors your need for rest, creation, socializing and reflection. By listening to your inner "seasons," you may also feel more connected to nature and the earthly rhythms that are bigger than you.

What?	Spring	Summer	Fall	Winter
When?	Follicular phase or waxing moon	Ovulation or full moon	Luteal phase or waning moon	Menstruation or new moon
Energy levels	Increasing	High-energy	Decreasing	Low-energy
Typical mood	Eager, flirty, creative, social, full of new ideas, curious, open	Out-going, confident, bold, passionate, sexy, bright	Focused, determined, more inward, sharp, emotional	Quiet, sensitive, raw, shy, tender, introverted, creative, intuitive
Best time for...	Starting projects, building teams, trying new things	Launching programs, sales, networking, public speaking	Finishing tasks, creating structure & systems	Reflecting on the previous cycle, dreaming, visioning

Getting Your Partner Onboard with Your Cycles

Oftentimes, when women come to understand the profound implications of their menstrual cycles, they want to share the information with their partners. I highly recommend this as your menstrual cycle, especially in heterosexual relationships, can set the emotional "tone" for your relationship.

When I started sharing my cycle with my current partner, the information was life-changing for him. He describes it this way,

"Knowing your menstrual cycle was like taking the red pill in the Matrix. Suddenly, everything made sense. I never could figure out why one week I was brilliant and you loved everything I did, and then shortly thereafter I could do nothing right. Learning your cycle was like learning a secret code to understanding women. Every man needs this information."

Communicating about your cycle is especially important if your partner is a man, as menstrual cycles may be foreign and mysterious territory to him.

What's possible when your partner understands and appreciates your cycle?

You feel understood. You feel less "crazy." You're more likely to be supported with your unique needs each week and are more likely to feel connected to your partner. You also develop a secret language together that can help you both understand what is happening.

Often women ask, "But how do I get him on board? He gets weirded out by these talks." It can be difficult to talk about your menstrual cycle, especially if you or your partner were not raised to speak openly about this. You or your partner may feel awkward discussing this together.

If that's true for you, here are a few things to consider:

1. Your partner mirrors you. If your partner dismisses your cycle as uninteresting or unimportant, it's possible you think the same thing. It's a good place to look—where do you not feel great about your cycle? Where do you feel embarrassed or ashamed of your hormonal changes? What support do you need to feel proud and right with your rhythm, first and foremost?

2. If you're with a man, let him know this information will help him "win" with you more often. As you will learn in Chapter 10, men have an innate drive to "win" with their female partners. He will feel as if he's successfully "won" with you when you're happy and open to him. So, let him know he'll feel more successful connecting with you once he understands how your needs and desires change week to week.

3. Lastly, never underestimate the power of humor. Your partner may be curious to know more but feel awkward asking. Bringing up your current "season" in a playful, humorous manner can make the whole topic of menstrual cycles feel more lighthearted and easier to talk about.

Exercise: Track Your Cycle

This simple exercise will help you become aware of how you change throughout the month. It is best done each day at the same time (morning or evening usually works best). If you skip a day or two, it's okay, just continue the next day. This will give you valuable self-awareness.

1. Grab a journal, the notes section in your phone or a menstrual tracking app such as Kindara.

2. Each day, write down the current day of your menstrual cycle. Remember: the first day you bleed is considered "Day 1." If you're tracking the moon, write down the current moon phase (this can be found via a Google search or an app like TimePassages).

3. Below the current phase, include notes about how you feel. Consider:

   a. How much energy did you have today (1-10, with 10 as very energetic)?

   b. How was your overall mood today?

   c. How social did you feel today?

   d. What types of activities felt really good today?

   e. What types of exercise and foods were you drawn to?

4. Continue taking notes each day for an entire cycle.

5. At the end of the cycle, read through your notes. What patterns or themes do you notice? What did you tend to want in each phase?

Exercise: Celebrate Your Bleeding

Does all of this information feel overwhelming or confusing? I get it. This exercise gives you a simple, easy place to start in honoring your cycles.

Celebrating your bleeding is still quite taboo throughout the world. The patriarchy teaches us to hide our bleeding and to feel ashamed of it. This exercise turns that script on its head by encouraging you to celebrate this time of month.

Choosing to celebrate your menstruation is a rebellious act of self-love and self-acceptance. This is a chance to be creative about how you can honor your femininity.

Here are a few ideas to celebrate your bleeding:

- Take a day off work to let yourself rest.
- Go on a mini-solo retreat.
- Wear a red bra under your work clothes.
- Pour your menstrual blood on the earth and say a prayer.
- Make an art project about lessons from the previous cycle.
- Create your own "red tent" by inviting other women over for tea and cookies.
- Write a vision for your future.
- Let yourself nap in the middle of the day.
- Watch your favorite romance movie.
- Buy fresh red roses for your desk.
- Put on red sheets.
- Read my favorite menstruation poem, *Down There* by *Sandra Cisneros*.

What ideas would you add? How can you celebrate your cycle this month?

Exercise: Full Moon Party

The full moon invites you to celebrate life's abundance.

Want to plan your own full moon celebration? A few ideas....

- Host a big party!
- Get dressed up with girlfriends.
- Go out dancing.
- Acknowledge yourself for your efforts.
- Buy yourself something you've been wanting.
- Plan a silly-themed dinner.
- Have a long lovemaking session with your beloved.
- Lay under the full moon and make wishes.

Now, look up when the next full moon is, and choose one of these activities to plan for that day. Have fun!

Invitation: Grab Your Journal

1. How do you feel about your menstrual cycle? Do you track and follow it? Does it feel foreign and weird or intimate and insightful?

2. What were you taught about menstruation growing up? What was your first period like?

3. What could it look like to organize your daily activities around your menstrual cycle? Even if you started small, what is one thing you could do to better follow your flow?

4. Do you want to share this information with your friends or intimate partner? What could that conversation look like?

Opening

"This is the truth in sacred relating: it seems like it's about your partner, but it's almost always about yourself. Your partner simply shows you the places where you are playing small, disempowered or otherwise compromised.

When you liberate those places and see your partner light up, you realize your full potential as a lover is back and that is exhilarating for both of you."

—London Angel Winters,
Awakened Woman's Guide to Everlasting Love

CHAPTER 11

MASCULINE AND FEMININE DYNAMICS

As we reclaim our feminine wildness and wisdom, we may find ourselves craving partnership. There is a certain type of growth that's only possible with another human. When we're in partnership, we come face-to-face with all the ways we prevent intimacy—the walls around our hearts, our insecurities, our fears and our shadow. Loving another human is a potent road to growth. At least, that was the case for me.

After settling in Bali, I felt ready to meet someone. I wanted to find a man with whom I could grow and build a life together. This next section is about my OPENING to love and the lessons I learned along the way. I hope you find it useful and inspiring, wherever you are in your love journey.

By this point, my coaching business was budding. I'd hired my first business coach, who was helping me design a logo, develop systems and create content. I was beginning to feel like an official entrepreneur.

My little Bali home was simple and beautiful, with crystals and flowers arranged exactly as I liked them. I felt connected with my desire, trusting what I wanted to do each day. I had begun making friends. I felt relaxed and in flow.

I wasn't actively searching for partnership, but I wasn't opposed to it, either. I was open to seeing what life had in store for me....

Meeting James on the Dance Floor

One Friday night, I decided to do what expats in Ubud, Bali do—go to ecstatic dance at Yoga Barn. This event seems to be a ritual for the community. Every Friday night, 150 people gather, sober and sweaty, to express themselves on the dance floor. I absolutely LOVE ecstatic dance.

I dressed in an outfit that made me feel sexy—a crochet top and short shorts—and hit the dance floor.

From across the room, I saw a man watching me. Not staring at me in a creepy way, but I could tell he was subtly observing me. I liked the feeling of his steady, subtle attention. We moved toward each other and began to dance. He was so present I felt as if the entire room melted away and all that was left was me and him. I know that sounds like a cliché, but it's true!

My body felt hot, gooey and electric. The intensity of the moment was almost too much, so I danced away from him. Then I missed him, and I came back. He remained steady the whole time, never chasing me or pressuring me.

I saw him dance with another woman and felt jealous. I wanted his attention for myself. We moved toward each other again.

During the last song, he slowed down our dance. He put his arms on my waist and held me close. I lifted up my head, offering myself to him. I felt wide open, turned on and totally trusting. He leaned down, hovered his lips over mine, not yet kissing me. My body felt flush with sensation. Finally, he slowly, slowly kissed me. I felt as if I was falling into that kiss. All I could feel was his lips. It was the best kiss of my life.

The sound healing began, so people laid down to listen. He guided me down to the ground, and I followed. I didn't know why, but I intuitively trusted him. Despite not even yet knowing his name, I felt loved, adored and safe. My body was a full *yes* to him, though I didn't know what the question was.

Little did I know I had just met my husband.

Masculine and Feminine Energy

I preface this chapter with my story of meeting James because that moment illustrates some of the concepts of masculine and feminine energy. Him leading, me following. Him initiating, me opening. Him responding, me expressing.

Before I get into this (highly charged) topic, I want you to know that when I say masculine/feminine, I do not mean man/woman. Masculine and feminine refers to energy that lives inside of all of us, regardless of gender or sexual orientation. We all have both masculine and feminine energy in us.

> *Masculine and feminine refers to energy that lives inside of all of us, regardless of gender or sexual orientation. We all have both masculine and feminine energy in us.*

Let me define the terms. Masculine energy is linear, directed, goal oriented, logical, factual. In contrast, feminine energy is intuitive, emotional, creative, sensitive, receptive, connected.

Put more poetically:
>She is the river. He is the bank that holds her.
>She is raw electric power. He is the direction in which power flows.
>She is deep, intuitive knowing. He is the logical explanation.
>She feels the desire. He is the structure that brings it to life.
>She is radiance and beauty. He is the one who witnesses and honors beauty.

Does that give you a sense of the two energies?

Another way to understand masculine and feminine is to associate these energies with a place. For example, Bali, my home, is full of wild jungle, natural beauty, temples and devotion. Flowers rain down from the sky and the rogue plants poke up through the sidewalk. The Balinese culture deeply values family, connection and a mystical relationship with the divine. The air is warm, humid and sensual. Everything feels more lush and saturated in Bali. In other words, I experience Bali as a feminine place.

Compare that to New York City. In NYC, people are walking quickly from A to B—they're on a mission. The streets are numbered in a logical sequence and make up a perfect, square grid. There's structure and orderliness to the city. Even the buildings are a bit phallic, penetrating straight up into the sky. I consider New York to be a more masculine place.

If you get the vibe of those two cities (New York vs. Bali), you can get a sense of what masculine vs. feminine are as energies.

Pause for a minute to reflect—which of these two energies are more expressed inside yourself right now? If there was a spectrum with NYC on one side and Bali the other, where would you be on that spectrum right now?

Help! I Hate the Words "Masculine" and "Feminine"

When I begin describing these terms, your hackles may immediately rise—and for good reason. The words "masculine" and "feminine" are highly emotionally charged, fraught with hundreds of years of oppression and disempowerment. These words come with a long history of sexism, rigid gender roles and violence against women. The words "masculine" and "feminine" are inherently polarizing.

If you feel uneasy or upset reading this chapter, you're not alone. I did, as well, when I first heard these terms. When reading my first book on masculine/feminine, I had to put my inner staunch femininist to the side in order to be open-minded enough to consider whether there may be any wisdom. Eventually, I found myself crying tears of understanding because I felt so much truth in this concept. It felt like coming home.

If you can't read the words "masculine" or "feminine" without cringing, here are two recommendations for you:

1. Go into the "hate" of masculine/feminine directly.
    a. What do these terms bring up in you?
    b. What resistance do you have to seeing the world this way?
    c. What does this resistance reveal about you?
    d. Whether or not you adopt these terms, investigating why the terms upset you can lead to powerful self-awareness.
2. An easier route? Just drop the terms. You can use less emotionally charged words such as "yin" and "yang", or "alpha" and "omega" to refer to the same universal duality of energy.

As with every concept in this book, I ask that you read this chapter with an open mind and then take what you like and leave the rest. Good?

Reclaiming My Feminine

My femininist parents did their best to raise me in a gender neutral way. For example, when I was five, they bought both my brother and me both race-car beds (even though I begged for the pink princess one), my dad taught me to ride a dirt bike early on and they encouraged me to learn karate, soccer and other traditionally "masculine" sports. They didn't want me to feel "boxed-in" to being a girly-girl.

Despite my parents' best efforts to not reinforce gender stereotypes, I felt drawn toward classically feminine activities including dolls, dresses and glitter. I loved singing and dancing for an audience. I choose to be a princess every single year for a decade on Halloween. I refused to wear blue jeans—only dresses. I loved animals. In my heart I was quite feminine.

Yet as I grew up, I noticed that certain traits were more valued by my teachers, parents and society than others. It appeared to be more important to be ambitious, goal-oriented, clear, concise and directed than to be creative, emotional, intuitive, sensual, dynamic and interconnected. For example, I got more attention for achieving an "A" than for being nurturing with our pets, creating beautiful art or having great intuition.

So, without any conscious thought, I began to shift from a sensitive, feminine little girl to an ambitious, decisive teenager. I raced to the top of each competition, becoming class president and valedictorian, yet at the cost of squashing my own feminine side. I repressed my emotions, didn't cry for a year and had very little sensuality. My mom would tease me about being a "brain on a stick," neglecting my body in pursuit of mental activity. Inside, I felt this unyielding pressure to do, do, do, as if I always had to be going somewhere.

When I began personal growth work, I discovered how much I had repressed my "feminine" in order to be successful in a masculine-dominated world. My emotions, my sensuality, my love of beauty, my nurturing side, my messy wildness...these parts of me were underused, underexpressed, and ultimately undervalued.

My story is not unique. There is a "masculinization" of women happening where in an effort to be taken more seriously as equals to men, many of us women overemphasize our masculine traits and suppress our feminine traits. This makes sense, given the context of living in a patriarchy, yet it has long-lasting and damaging consequences.

What is "Powerful Feminine?"

When I began doing personal growth work, I started deliberately reclaiming my feminine side.

One day, my coach asked me, "What does 'powerful feminine' look like to you?"

Honestly, I was stumped.

I knew what a powerful masculine looked like and what a little girl looked like, but a powerful, grown-up feminine? I couldn't see her.

My coach continued, encouraging me to recall powerful feminine role models from movies. I couldn't think of any! Can you? Mulan, Wonderwoman, Katniss Everdeen from the Hunger Games? They are all women acting in their masculine energy (literally by becoming a man in Mulan).

I still struggle to find powerful feminine role models in movies. Maybe Moana is the closest I can think of, as she trusts her intuition, works with nature and loves the "villain" back into goodness. In the end, Moana's connection with the feminine saves Mother Earth—a powerful potential for all of us.

Living in a patriarchy, we have very few role models for a woman who is both feminine AND powerful. Given our cultural context, these two words can almost feel like a contradiction, as if to be feminine is to be inherently weak.

This is not true.

I've come to believe that "powerful feminine" looks like ...

- Knowing what we want and asking for it with full vulnerability
- Graciously receiving love, attention and opportunities
- Embracing the wisdom in our emotions
- Powerfully and lovingly laying down boundaries

- Inviting our partners and ourselves into a higher standard of behavior
- Loving others generously, without caretaking and fixing
- Connecting with nature—earth, animals, plants, seasons
- Listening to our bodies and letting ourselves be guided by a deeper intelligence
- Following our natural cycles of growth and contraction
- Enjoying the magnetism of our beauty and sex while being responsible for its impact
- Naming the truth we feel, even if it is subtle or we feel crazy
- Fully trusting our desires, especially when they don't "make sense"
- Fiercely protecting what and who we love when needed, like a mama bear
- Speaking boldly and passionately about what we believe in
- Creating exuberantly—art, projects, babies, etc.—gestating and birthing our whole lives

What comes up for you reading this? Can you relate to some of these "powerful feminine" items? Which are most challenging for you to embody?

Healthy Masculine, Healthy Feminine

To thrive, we need both a healthy masculine and a healthy feminine side. Above, I described a powerful (or healthy) feminine. What does "unhealthy" feminine look like?

Unhealthy feminine energy may look like...

- Creating emotional chaos and drama
- Being petty and jealous
- Demanding to be taken care of
- Acting passive or helpless ("damsel in distress")

- Manipulating others
- Using sex appeal for personal gain
- Communicating passive aggressively
- Overly caretaking and smothering
- Acting like a martyr due to lack of boundaries

Now, what about masculine energy? What are the healthy and unhealthy versions of masculinity?

To me, healthy masculine looks like …

- Protecting and providing for those you love
- Standing for a deeper truth or cause in which you believe
- Setting clear, unambiguous boundaries
- Knowing your worth and asking for it
- Speaking and acting in the face of injustice
- Loving and respecting the feminine
- Being present and sensitive to the moment
- Tuned into nature and the surroundings
- Staying strong in the face of challenges or obstacles
- Fighting for what you believe in
- Refusing to tolerate bad behavior
- Loyal and committed
- Engaging in healthy competition that brings out the best in both of you

Meanwhile, unhealthy masculine looks like…

- Greedily taking more than your "fair share"
- Dominating and controlling others and resources
- Competing to be the best (while hurting others)
- Demanding great treatment without offering respect
- Resentfully giving to those you love

- Being militantly self-reliant, "the lone warrior"
- Pretending to be solid on the outside but feeling weak inside
- Ignorant or uncaring of your actions
- Prioritizing personal or financial gain over others' wellbeing
- Ruthless in achieving goals
- Unwilling to help others if it puts you in harm's way
- Speaking more than doing

Ideally, you want both masculine and feminine to be healthy and in balance inside of you. This balance may not be fifty/fifty of each energy (more on that later in "You Have a Home Base").

On a tangible level, all of creation comes from the masculine/feminine union—so if you want to create something, you *have* to get these two parts of you working together to make it happen.

What does this "inner union" look like? Let's explore...

How Your Inner Masculine and Feminine Work Together

Our feminine side feels the answer instinctually and intuitively,
A clear *yes* or *no* inside her body,
A tightening in her gut or heart, a softening in her belly,
Even without knowing all the information around it.
She senses the "vibe" and responds to it either with trust or distrust.
She says, "Yes" or, "No."

Our masculine side needs to test the idea,
Hold it up to his deeper values and bigger picture,
Filter it through, sort it out,
Make sure the logistics line up,
The finances, the time, the people.
He says, "How?"

This dynamic happens inside us as our inner masculine and inner feminine work out major decisions such as getting married, quitting our jobs or moving to a new city.

Both our inner masculine and our inner feminine need to weigh in. Her intuition gives direction to his planning.

Here's where the trouble starts—
When one side undervalues or dismisses the other's wisdom. For example...

- When we feel an immediate *yes* (our feminine wisdom) and then start second-guessing or doubting if we can actually do it, letting logistics (masculine wisdom) crowd out our intuitive knowing.

- When we feel distrust around a new person (feminine wisdom) but rationally convince ourselves it is okay (masculine wisdom)—and find out later that our instincts were right.

- When we get so excited about a new business idea (feminine wisdom) and pour all our resources into it without doing any market research (masculine wisdom) and then find ourselves drowning in debt a few months later.

We need to access both our masculine and our feminine wisdom.

We need our inner feminine instincts, intuition and desires to give us the *yes/no*—to show us where to direct our focus. We need our inner masculine intellect, planning and logistics to help us figure out how to do the things and what it will take to make them happen.

When these two parts of ourselves work together, in union, it's magic.

Finding union between these sides of ourselves so we can make powerful decisions is not easy, but the magic that results from this inner union is SO worth it.

When these parts of you work well internally, you'll find greater masculine/feminine union in your intimate relationships, as well. When these energies trust each other in a relationship, it becomes an exquisite dance, taking you both places you could not go alone.

You Have a Home Base

This is controversial, but I'll say it anyway—you have a home base inside of either masculine or feminine energy.

While we all hold both masculine and feminine energies, most of us are not meant to express these energies in exactly a 50% masculine and 50% feminine ratio.

Instead, imagine a piano. While a skilled pianist can play up and down the keys, they still have a "home base" where the keys feel easiest and most natural for their fingers to play. Similarly, you can play higher notes and lower notes to create beautiful music, yet you still have a section of the keys toward which you gravitate.

Masculine/feminine energy works the same way. Ideally, we **can** express very masculine and very feminine energy depending on the environment and the needs of the situation. Yet, we still have a "home base," a particular place on the spectrum that feels most natural to us.

If your "home base" is more feminine, your primary concern in life will be love-oriented. To share love, express love, to connect, to nurture and to create. If your "home base" is more masculine, you will focus more on freedom and how to achieve your mission and purpose on earth.

Why does it matter to know your "home base?"

Because knowing your home base can help you create situations that feel most natural to you, where your inherent gifts can shine.

To explain, let's say you work as an accountant or lawyer, where the workplace culture requires you to spend more time in your masculine energy (analyzing, arguing, thinking, etc.), which is great, but if you're doing that every day, day after day, week after week, month after month, year after year, you can get stuck expressing mostly masculine energy.

Do we need to stop doing "masculine" jobs like being an accountant or a lawyer? No way. Once you understand these terms, you can consciously create situations for your feminine energy to express, such as making an effort to get to know your coworkers more personally or taking breaks to stretch your body, drink delicious sweet-smelling tea and nurturing your office's new hires. These small actions can help you feel more "at home" in a masculine-dominated world.

Understanding how to move between your own masculine and feminine energy is important everywhere in your life—yet nowhere more important than in your intimate relationships. To this end, let me tell you a little client story...

Masculine and Feminine in Dating

Rani Begins to Date

Rani was a tech executive in her early thirties managing a full team. She had graduated from the most elite universities and her resume was top notch.

Unfortunately? She struggled to find and keep a man. She told me that rarely were men "good enough" for her, as she tended to be smarter and more accomplished than they were. When she did find a man she liked, his interest in her always waned after a few months.

She couldn't figure it out. She was so frustrated that all her intellectual prowess wasn't helping her solve the riddle of finding a husband. So, she hired me.

I taught her about masculine vs. feminine energies and she quickly identified that she was primarily running on her masculine energy.

She was goal-oriented even in dating. ("I need to find a partner as quickly as possible, with minimal effort and wasted time.") She often made the first move, clearly asserting what she wanted. While these are incredible traits that had certainly helped her in business, they weren't helping her attract a masculine partner.

Regardless of gender, masculine energy attracts feminine energy and vice versa. When she approached dating with masculine energy, she would either a) find feminine men to date, or b) repel the masculine men she wanted.

The antidote? Letting her feminine energy primarily express in dating.

Rani and I began working on taking down the armor around her heart. For example, she had a habitual tendency to protect the tenderness of her heart by jumping into her head and analyzing the situation, then giving commands to others.

We worked on:

- Dismantling the way she stays safe by intellectualizing instead of feeling
- Letting go of control and trusting another person's sense of direction
- Being vulnerable enough to ask for help and share her desires
- Opening to let a man impact her and touch her heart
- Reclaiming her sensuality and feeling safe to be sensual around men

These are tectonic level shifts. These protective patterns were built over thirty-five years and weren't dismantled in a few mere weeks. But week after week, she continued to show up, challenge herself, reflect and do the practices we worked on.

Within six weeks, she found a man she liked and respected, and they began to date seriously. She let herself soften and receive his affection, blushing and flushing in ways I hadn't yet seen her do. She looked lit up from the inside out, full of radiance.

This new level of intimacy was scary for her and often she would revert back to taking over control, commanding him, intellectualizing the situation, etc. But together, we would catch that old pattern and gently return to her new aim of showing up with feminine energy in dating.

Rani and her new partner didn't stay together forever—they broke up after six months—but it gave her a powerful chance to practice OPENING to love. Now, she is more ready than ever for her next relationship.

Sometimes we expect our "happily ever after" to happen once we "find the one," but in my experience, grown-up relating is different. It requires us to see our relationships as playgrounds to learn and develop, places to shed old patterns and practice new, more loving behaviors. So in every relationship, no matter how long or short, if we've been learning inside of it, it is a success.

Why Modern Women Struggle to Find Masculine Partners

(Note: I will refer mostly to heterosexual relationships, as that is my experience and that of the women I've worked with so far. If your arrangement is different, please substitute genders and pronouns.)

Often I coach women when they're in their early to mid thirties who are professionally successful and ambitious. Like Rani, they're driven to achieve yet can't quite find or keep a masculine partner.

Why is this?

Well, because these women are providing their own masculine energy. They know where they're going. They're self-sufficient, self-reliant and take charge. Their masculine side is probably stronger than most men's masculine.

Does this mean you're doomed in dating if you're professionally successful?

Absolutely not. It just means that you may need to be "energetically flexible," bringing your masculine to the workplace and your powerful feminine into dating.

Remember that feminine attracts masculine and vice versa. Imagine a battery with a positive and negative end. The difference between the two ends creates the electrical current which gives the battery its power. The same "current" happens between a person expressing strong masculine energy and someone expressing strong feminine energy. That's called polarity.

Polarity feels like "the spark" or a surge of attraction. People describe it as two people "having chemistry." To create that spark with a masculine person, you must embody feminine energy.

If you primarily want to be in your feminine energy in love and you want to find a masculine partner, I have three tips for you:

1. **Trust him.** Believe him when he says he's going to do something. Believe he will show up on time. Trust his intentions. Unless you have a clear red flag such as addiction, cheating or deep gambling debt, etc., allow yourself to trust him wholeheartedly. More on this in the following chapter.

2. **Surrender to his sense of direction.** A great salsa dance requires a lead and a follow. When you allow him to create the plans, organize the logistics and direct the activity of the partnership, you can relax and be delightfully surprised by what might unfold.

3. **Express moment-to-moment.** The only way the masculine becomes a good "lead" with you is if you show him moment-to-moment how his presence and decisions feel to you. Demonstrate if his decisions feel trustworthy and pleasurable (or not), using your face, body and tone of voice. This third point is critical because it provides a "check" on the first two points.

232

Remember that these three tips only apply when you want to be in your feminine energy—following, surrendering, feeling, opening. There will be times when you'd rather be in your masculine energy—directing, leading, deciding—and that is great!

Let's put these three tips into context. Imagine you're being asked out on a third date. He suggests Chinese food. You don't want to go to Chinese food but you do want to surrender to his sense of direction. What do you do?

You could say, "No, I don't want to go there. Why don't we go to that Italian place instead?" This would put you in the masculine role of deciding and directing your activities.

Another option is that when he says, "Let's go to Chinese food," you can make a face that shows you're not so into the idea. If he's perceptive, he'll pick up on that and try again, perhaps by suggesting Italian.

If he's not so perceptive, you can say something more direct like, "Ahh...I'm not really feeling that. Where else can we go?"

If you have a specific desire, say for Italian, feel free to suggest it! Such as, "You know what I'd love? I'm craving spaghetti from that Italian place." Then let him plan and organize the rest.

Being in your feminine means giving him clues or words about your desires without taking over and directing the experiences. It's a softer, more open, playful way of relating.

Let's continue with the date analogy to demonstrate Tip #1 on trusting him. Allow yourself to trust that he will show up on time, that he will be prepared and will treat you well. Soften into that.

Now, if he doesn't show up on time, you don't have to be "chill" and say, "That's fine, no worries," (unless it actually is to you). No, you're allowed to show him that him being late upset you. Use primarily your face and body, *showing* him more than *telling* him. Words will bring both of you into your mind and into stories where defensiveness and judgment lie. Instead, show him moment-to-moment as honestly and accurately as you can how your heart is impacted by him. Then he has the information he needs on how to show up and skillfully guide both of you.

Remember, feminine energy is not something you're putting on from the outside. "Being feminine" is not a particular way you're meant to dress or a particular way you're meant to be. No. Your feminine energy is already inside of you, waiting to be discovered and expressed.

"Why Would I Surrender to a Man?"

Earlier in the chapter, I explained how being in your feminine energy means surrendering part of your sense of direction to your masculine partner.

Understandably, this idea can bring up resistance, fear and disagreement. Women have finally begun to gain independence—financially, emotionally and socially—from men. We have a long history of not being equals, of being subservient to men, and frankly, we still have a long way to go. I can understand why you'd feel, "No way. I don't want to give that up. I've just got this level of freedom." Your sisters, your mothers, your grandmothers, your great grandmothers all fought for this freedom.

If you feel uncomfortable about the concept of surrendering to a man, a couple of notes:

1. **You don't surrender everything about you.** You don't surrender your boundaries, your needs or your desires. So what do you surrender? You surrender the part of you that wants to control the dynamic in a relationship. Why? Because in order to have sexual attraction, there must be two poles in any given moment, one leading and one following.

2. Realize you're not only sacrificing when you surrender—**you're gaining a wild, beautiful sexual intimacy and attraction**. It is important to realize why there's a reason to surrender, that is not just because you "should be" more

feminine. F*ck that, you can be whatever you want to be. It's not because you have to be in a relationship, because you don't have to be. It's because you say, and it's a very bold declaration, that "I'm going to surrender part of my control for the sake of love."

3. Even if you choose to surrender controlling the dynamics or directing the partnership, **you are not powerless**. In fact, the feminine IS the power source. Your joy, your radiance, your displeasure, your hurt...these are the signals your partner uses to learn to better navigate the "boat" of the relationship. Your emotional expression is the wisdom that guides his direction.

"My Masculine Side Is Stronger Than His."

In some ways, women are a little ahead of the curve right now. Graduating from top universities faster than men. Out-earning men in entry level positions. If you're an ambitious woman, you may feel "smarter" or more successful than the men you meet, just as Rani did in the above story. There's some truth to it. But that's not the truth that will help you.

When you hold the story in your mind and in your body that *no man is smart enough* or *I can 'be masculine' better than he can*, you will find evidence for that story. You will attract less competent and less successful men while repelling smart, capable men.

It's important to question this story and realize it is not true all of the time. This story is often a protective mechanism against true, deep intimacy, because it prevents any man from getting too close. So you can see this story for what it is—sometimes true, but more often protective armoring around the soft tissues of your heart.

Masculine and Feminine in Long-Term Love

Imagine you've been dating for a while, and you found a partner you love. Congratulations!

Now, how do you keep the spark and passion alive for the long-term?

By using the same skills around masculine/feminine that you used to attract your partner in the first place. Let me tell you a story about how one couple I worked with reignited their sexual spark using these concepts.

Nia and Jalen

Nia and Jalen were a powerful entrepreneurial couple who taught meditation to hundreds of people. They worked together, lived together and raised a dog together.

And yet, unfortunately, they weren't having great sex together.

They were trying to conceive a baby, so when they did have sex, it was purposeful, practical act, and only when she was ovulating.

Nia and Jalen came to James and me for help on their sexuality.

The first thing I noticed is how often Nia (the woman) took control of the situation. She hired me, paid me, signed the contract and was the first person to describe the problem. Her husband (Jalen) took a back seat, looking a bit lost and confused. Their dynamic had Nia firmly in her masculine energy of directing and deciding, while Jalen was in a more passive and following role.

During our second session, I asked them to look into each other's eyes. I encouraged Jalen to feel himself becoming grounded, strong and rooted, while I invited Nia to melt, soften and begin to gently move. Jalen sat upright, proud and still, fully present and drinking Nia in, while Nia brought her attention down into the soft curves of her belly, hips and thighs. She began to undulate her spine, bringing waves into her body.

Of course, at first, both Nia and Jalen felt awkwardly self-conscious doing this, as many people do when they try something for the first time. However, Nia and Jalen also felt more masculine and more feminine than they had in years. She blushed and smiled. He looked strong and powerful. The spark returned to both of their eyes.

Over the course of three months, we taught them many different exercises to bring more polarity into their relationship, which is the deliberate use of masculine/feminine energy to create sexual spark or chemistry.

It worked! They had the best sex of their entire eleven-year relationship while working with us. She orgasmed for the first time without a vibrator, and best of all, they loved making love again. Sex moved from a functional activity for conceiving a baby toward a celebration of their love.

This is what's possible when we understand masculine/feminine dynamics. Learning these concepts and tools can shed light on why the sexual spark dies down and how to bring it back.

The Best Buddies Syndrome

One of the most common dynamics I see in relationships is the Best Buddy Syndrome (my personal name for this).

When your relationship started, maybe you had a lot of sexual attraction and chemistry. It may have felt juicy, electric and exciting.

As time went on, you two may have become more and more similar—similar hobbies, friends, food, lifestyles. Which is lovely, as similarity can be the foundation of emotional closeness in relationships.

Unfortunately, sameness erodes erotic attraction. Your natural polarity, the masculine/feminine differences between you and your partner, has smoothed out and resulted in less charge.

When you've become a great team but lack erotic attraction, you're in the "Muddy Middle" where neither of you are particularly masculine nor feminine. The muddy middle lacks polarity and feels like best friends, roommates or business partners.

The good news?

If the spark was there in the beginning of your relationship, you can always rediscover it. Reigniting sexual polarity simply requires the right perspective and tools.

One simple way to begin is to celebrate the *differences* between you two. Celebrate how the masculine partner is steady and solid with a clear trustable direction. Celebrate how the feminine partner is dynamic, intuitive, sexy and beautiful with a powerful heart. As you honor your differences, you make space to rediscover each other anew, in a more polarized way.

Polarity—Your New Relationship Superpower

Once you understand these basic concepts, you have a superpower most of the world does not—you can drop into either polarity at any time.

For example:
If you need to get sh*t done and hit your goals, you can draw upon your masculine.
If you want to nurture yourself or others, you can draw upon your feminine.

You have just made the deep energetics inside yourself conscious and in that consciousness, you can deliberately play with your own energy, drawing out the parts you need in any given moment. Cool, right?

Here's how...

If you want to drawn upon your **masculine** energy, here are a few ways:

- Set a goal and work toward that goal in a disciplined, focused manner
- Meditate and observe your thoughts in a detached way
- Compete with someone, especially physically, as in sports
- Analyze a situation from multiple perspectives
- Commit fully to a new daily practice and do it whether you "feel" like it or not
- Challenge yourself by taking on a physically difficult task like running a marathon, lifting a heavy weight or climbing a mountain
- Take command of a group situation and tell them where to go
- Feel your solidity, stability and strength
- Make decisive, clear decisions for yourself and others

The way you access your masculine energy will be unique, so feel free to use that list as inspiration only, rather than as a prescription, and add your own ideas.

Now let's explore your feminine.

A few ways to access your **feminine** energy:

- Play with a pet, noticing its different moods and needs
- Nurture a plant and watch it grow
- Move your body in a sensual way, opening yourself up to experiencing pleasure
- Make your emotions a priority (e.g. through Swamping practice from Chapter 8)
- Meditate while feeling the dynamic sensations in your body

- Swim in the ocean and let the waves move you
- Walk in lush natural settings and feel connected to nature
- Take a long, sensual bath with epsom salts, essential oils and candles
- Ask for help with a difficult task (like moving homes, repairing a bike, etc.)
- Receive compliments graciously
- Adorn your body with clothing, jewelry and make up that makes you feel beautiful
- Let the situation impact you and express the impact it has
- Take time to explore your desires
- Surrender to another person's leadership (who feels trustworthy!)
- Trust your intuition even when it doesn't "make sense"
- Breathe into your pussy
- Soften your belly, pelvis and throat
- Learn to sing and feel your voice ripple through your body
- Create art, allowing the colors and textures to move you
- Learn intuitive tools like tarot or crystal readings

There are so many ways to get back in touch with your feminine. As you create your own list on how to access your feminine, consider the five essences of the feminine as inspiration—emotion, intuition, sensuality, movement and beauty. In addition, all of Section 2 ("Reclaiming") is about discovering your feminine.

"How Do I Get Him to Appreciate My Masculine?"

So far, I've discussed the importance of being in your feminine energy to attract a masculine partner. Yet, this is only half the equation. What happens when you enter into a long-term partnership? Must you deny half of you (your masculine) in order to keep him interested?

Definitely not.

To be whole, you must have full access to all parts of you. That means being fully in your masculine when needed (such as kicking ass on your work deadline), and then being fully in your feminine when needed (such as nurturing your children).

A great partner will love and respect all of these sides of you. He will want you to be whole, and visa versa. Ideally, you embrace his feminine sides as well, welcoming his emotions, vulnerability, intuition and desires. That's a wholehearted partnership.

While he respects your masculine, a masculine-oriented partner may not feel **turned on** by you when you're in masculine mode. That's okay. When I'm sitting down to write this book, I'm on a mission and I get quite "masculine." James is not necessarily sexually attracted to me like this, yet he loves this side of me and appreciates my ability to get things done. When I want to flirt with and seduce James again, say on a writing break, I'll draw out my feminine energy.

Enjoy being in your masculine. Demand respect for your masculine. Yet, don't expect him to feel sexually attracted to your masculine.

Don't Weaponize the Terms

One last note on masculine/feminine for now...

It can be tempting to use these concepts to feel not good enough about yourself ("I should be more feminine") or to be judgmental towards a partner ("Why is he not more masculine?"). It can be especially tempting in a heterosexual partnership to assume that the man should be "masculine" and the woman should be "feminine," yet this is limiting and overly simplistic.

Please don't do that.

It is not kind to yourself or to your partners to weaponize these terms. You and your partner should be nothing other than what you are. If you are curious to explore a particular energy, great! If you're content with the way these energies express through you currently, great.

We're not in the 1950's. We're not trying to get back into rigid gender roles and put the whole of who we are into a narrow box of what is "masculine" vs. "feminine." No.

We contain multitudes, and like a diamond, we have infinite complexity in how our soul can express itself. When we try to force ourselves (or our partners) to conform to some idea of "feminine" or "masculine," we discount our wholeness and cause disharmony inside ourselves.

Rather than trying to stuff your or your partner's wholeness into a box, instead notice what you're each naturally great at doing. Then give yourself permission to thrive in that role while leaning on your partner to handle what you're not great at doing. A relationship is a team with each person bringing their strengths to the table.

Allow these energies to move fluidly between you two, where there is space for each of you to play the "masculine" or the "feminine" role at different times.

Invitation: Grab Your Journal

1. Which energy do you express more often—masculine or feminine? What does that look like?

2. Which energy do you want to embody more of?

3. When you're dating or in a relationship, does your partner show up predominantly in their masculine energy or in their feminine energy? What does this say about the energy you bring to a relationship?

4. What energy would you like to bring more of into your intimate relationship? How could you do that?

Meditation: Masculine/Feminine

Background

Both masculine and feminine coexist inside of you to create wholeness. This meditation gives you an embodied experience of what each of these energies feel like so when you want to experience either masculine or feminine energy, you know how.

The below meditation is available in audio format, for free, on my website: **www.megandlambert.com/book**.

Instructions

Find a seat and close your eyes. Take a deep breath.

Scan your entire body. How are you feeling right now?

When you're ready, begin to feel the solid rigidity of your spine.

Your spine holds you up with its strength and its power. Feel the vertebrae stacking on top of each other like a mountain. Feel the deep solidity of your spine, a part of you that stays relatively the same throughout your life. Your bones are very stable, solid parts of you. As you breathe in, continue to feel as if you're resting back against this solid core of your spine.

Witness your thoughts as they come and go. Witness sensations arise and fall without being drawn into them—just witnessing.

Noticing your breath. Feeling solid. Steady. Unchanging. The witness.

This is your masculine energy.

Take a deep breath and shake your arms, your legs and your spine. Let that go.

Now it's time to feel your feminine.

This time, breathe in and let your body move with the breath. Feel the rise of your inhale and the exhale that sinks you back down. You move your spine in gentle undulations. Wave your chest forward on the inhale and on the exhale soften back.

As you breathe, notice the soft tissues along the front of your body. The softness of your throat, your chest, diaphragm, belly, hips, pussy. Breathe them open.

Feel the blood and the liquids of your body. Notice how most of your body is water. Let yourself move and sway, absorbed in the sensation. If emotions arise, let yourself go into that emotion fully. Sadness, joy, frustration, irritation— let yourself fully feel the emotion and express it through your whole body.

You might make faces, curling your body inward or pushing your chest outward depending on how you're feeling. Move. Breathe. Feel dynamic and liquidy, in touch with your emotions and your sensuality.

Bring your hands to touch your skin and caress your body. Notice places of pleasure.

This is your feminine.

This is the part of you that's emotion, intuition and sensuality. She's watery, changing and powerful in her fluidity.

Take one more breath to breathe in your feminine. Notice that this too is a meditation. We're often taught to meditate in a very masculine way by sitting still rigidly and observing the experience. Yet being fully taken by your emotions and your sensuality is meditation, as well.

Once you finish the meditation, take a minute to notice: which of these two ways of meditating felt easier for you? Which felt more challenging? Do any thoughts or judgments come up about either one? Just notice.

Remember that you are whole.

You contain both your strong, steady masculine and your fluid, ever-changing feminine. You have both, and get a choice in which side to bring out at any given moment. Enjoy the exploration.

Exercise: Feminine Responsiveness

Responsiveness and sensitivity is a feminine gift. In the purest form, she allows life to touch her moment-to-moment. When she's happy, she bursts into a genuine smile. When she's sad, she lets tears fall from her eyes without shame. When she's angry, she stomps and crosses her arms.

If you've ever seen a little girl react instantly to her environment, moment-to-moment, you've seen this level of responsiveness. This level of full expression is our inherent feminine gift, though many of us have learned to repress our natural response in order to "be appropriate" or not seem "crazy."

In partnership, the feminine can cultivate and gift her responsiveness to her masculine partner by showing him moment-to-moment how he is impacting her. This gives him critical information on how he is showing up.

At an overt level, this responsiveness may look like frowning or making a discontented sound when he goes to check his phone in the middle of the conversation, indicating a lack of presence. At a more subtle level, she may cringe when she feels him mentally check out while she talks about her day, even if he is still nodding and smiling, appearing to be listening. She can feel when he is not really "with" her energetically.

This exercise will help you cultivate the ability to notice and respond, moment-to-moment, to a masculine partner's level of presence.

1. Choose a partner to practice with who will play the masculine role. This can be your intimate partner or a friend who's open to trying this. As we all have both energies, this person can be any gender.
2. Set a timer for seven minutes.

3. Sit across from each other and look into each other, focusing on each other's left eyes (so you're not awkwardly flipping back and forth between each other's eyes).

4. Feel your breath and your body. Settle in together.

5. Now, masculine partners, modulate how attentive you are. Spend a few minutes truly present with your partner, then let your mind drift a bit before returning to presence. Notice the impact that has.

6. If you're the feminine partner, actively notice and exaggerate how you feel in response to your masculine partner's presence.

   o If your partner is present with you, you might smile or blush with pleasure or even let out a little moan. Feel your natural response to this person's attention and amplify it.

   o If your partner is checked out, in their head, thinking, etc., notice how that impacts your heart and let them know using your face and body language. A frown, a frustrated sound, a pained expression, etc. Continue until your partner "comes back" to full presence with you.

7. Continue until the timer ends.

8. When the timer goes off, do a small bow to each other.

9. Reflect by taking turns, sharing, "What I loved about this was …" and "What I discovered was …"

10. If you'd like to, you can also switch roles and try on the "masculine" part.

Remember: It feels so good when your partner is fully present with you. But no partner will **ever** be fully present with you, always. It doesn't matter how much work he has done on himself. Feeling disappointed, frustrated or pained is part of intimate relating. Your gift as the feminine partner is to show that pain and to nonverbally invite him back into presence with you.

CHAPTER 12

TRUSTING THE MASCULINE

When we are in our healthiest feminine expression, we draw forward the healthy masculine expression in our partners. Healthy masculine has an impulse to protect and provide, to ensure we are safe and well-cared for. The best in the feminine brings out the best in the masculine.

Yet this healthy masculine can only emerge when we decide to trust our partners. Our trust reveals our partner's brilliance. It is incredibly scary and brave to decide to trust someone and open our hearts to love. This chapter explores the challenge—and rewards—of that journey.

Trusting James to Help Me in Australia

After that surprising, sexy meeting on the dance floor, James and I began seeing each other regularly. It was casual, with neither of us looking for a partner. We each cherished our independence and the way we were discovering ourselves as single beings.

Yet it was also undeniable that we were beginning to feel deep love for each other. Day by day, I felt more attached to him.

A few months after we first met, James left for Australia to do a month-long training program. I asked if I could join him for a few days. He was touched and said, "Of course!"

He found an Airbnb he thought I would love, full of plants with a big yard. He planned the whole trip and kept the details a secret so that when I landed in Australia I'd be whisked away for a trip of his creation. It was all quite romantic.

Unfortunately, the universe had other plans for us. I landed in Australia at 11pm that night and discovered I had several missed calls from James. Uh-oh, something wasn't right. I called him immediately.

"My flight was canceled. I tried to buy another but they are all sold out. I tried to rent a car and drive the eight hours to see you, but the cars were all reserved. I'm booked on another flight for tomorrow morning, but it means I can't join you tonight. I'm so sorry," he said.

"Oh! It's okay. I can figure out a hotel for the night. I'll see you in the morning," I said. I was disappointed but relaxed about it. As a consultant who has traveled the world many times solo, finding and booking a hotel for myself in a new country was no problem.

"Why don't you let me?" he offered.

I paused. Let him find and book me a hotel? Hmm. I couldn't deny that I felt a little turned on by the idea. I also felt stubborn, thinking, "Does he think I'm some damsel in distress?! I can do this myself."

However, I was actively working on graciously receiving masculine support, so I responded simply, "Thank you. That would be wonderful." My cheeks flushed and I felt hot, a little sweaty. It was a generous offer to accept.

A few minutes later, he called me back. "I just booked you a room at this hotel. It's simple, elegant and downtown, so you can explore Sydney while you wait for me. Your Uber is on its way to pick you up at the airport."

This was so much to receive, I almost cried. Here I was, a stubbornly self-reliant woman, letting this man handle the logistics and take care of me. I knew, of course, I could have done all of this on my own, yet having him take care of these details made me feel loved and cared for.

That was the start of an amazing week together which led me to realize I was ready to be in a more committed relationship with him.

Have you let yourself receive support from the masculine like that before? What did it feel like?

Why It Is Challenging to Trust the Masculine

Relying on another person's masculine energy so you can be more in your feminine energy is no easy feat, especially if you're a strong, independent woman. Surrender and trust may not come easily to you.

This makes sense, when considering that for thousands of years, men have objectified, degraded and oppressed women. So naturally, many women have inherited some suspicions of masculinity.

In addition, the recent movement around #metoo and toxic masculinity has made women even more wary of men, and rightly so. We're in a cultural reckoning around the damages of immature masculine and sexist oppression.

This has created a generation of women who are distrustful of their masculine partners, who won't let themselves relax into his leadership, trust his direction or let themselves be taken by masculine energy. Which has created a whole lot of women who are lonely in love.

So, if you feel skeptical of masculinity, that makes sense. My invitation is to journal on:

1. What stories or beliefs do you have about the masculine?

2. Where do these beliefs come from? What experiences have you had that led you to this conclusion about masculinity and men?

3. What would it be like to trust (healthy) masculinity and draw that energy forward in people you date?

(Note: refer to Chapter 3 - Questioning Your Stories - for more insight on how to work with stories around men and masculinity.)

You may have been deeply hurt by the masculine or hold (justified) rage against men. Yet, your anger or distrust towards the masculine won't serve you in love; it will cause pain, bitterness, and discontent. Letting down your guard and taking the risk to trust the (healthy) masculine is essential if you want to choose partnership.

Bottom line: if you want to be loved by men...you must learn to love men and trust masculinity.

Discerning If Someone Is Trustworthy

Your feminine gift is to open, to yield, to allow, to surrender. But I am not going to recommend you open like this to just anyone and trust them fully. No, there is a key element of discernment needed to stay safe and sane in love.

When meeting a new partner, consider ...

- Does this person show up on time and honor his commitments?
- Does this person follow through on his word?
- Does this person lie or hide the truth?
- Does this person feel stable, steady and reliable?

All of these factors are important to consider before you give a partner your trust. Your intuition is your best guidance here *(see Chapter 2 on trusting your body's yes and no)*.

Often, when I work with clients who have had a history of troubling past relationships, we uncover that they had a suspicion in the beginning that their previous partner wasn't trustworthy. Their intuition picked up on something but they didn't listen, and they ended up in a troubling situation.

You can learn about your tendencies to over-trust or under-trust potential partners by examining your past relationships. What led to your previous break-ups? What traits does a partner need in order for you to fully trust that person?

For example, before I met James, my two or three previous partners before him were all in deep debt. They struggled to make money, and as I can be deliciously codependent, I ended up supporting them financially. This eroded my sense of trust in their ability to take care of themselves.

I decided I didn't want that distrusting dynamic in my next relationship. So early on, I asked James, "Tell me about your financial situation. Are you deeply in debt?"

He wasn't, and then I asked, "Can you explain how you make money and where you choose to spend your money?" I wanted to understand his values around money and if we were aligned. Through my previous relationships, I had learned how important financial stability was in helping me feel safe in trusting my masculine partner, so I asked upfront.

Your criteria to trust a partner may be different. For example, maybe you and your last partner were disconnected sexually, and you didn't enjoy the same types of touch. Perhaps his touch hurt, and you couldn't soften into his touch. So when looking for your next relationship, you might notice how potential partners move, eat their food and touch you. This will give you clues on whether or not you may enjoy his flavor of sensuality, and if it could be something you could soften into.

It is important to remember that this is not necessarily a reaction against your exes so much as a deeper exploration of who you are and what you need in order to trust someone. By looking at what has caused us trouble in our past relationships, we can understand what our values and needs are and then find a partner who is a better match for us moving forward.

By moving slowly in love, we can stay alert for potential red flags.

Here are a few other key indicators I looked at when deciding if I could trust James:

1. **Did he have a close group of male friends?** Has he been friends with these people for a while? This is often a good sign that he shows up reliably for people he loves. (James did.)

2. **Does he have any addictions?** I've dated men with addiction problems in the past and I know how disruptive this can be for a relationship, so it was paramount to me that a potential future husband wasn't struggling with any major addictions. (James didn't.)

3. **What's his relationship with his family like?** My relationship with my family is very important to me, and I wanted to find a man who had a similarly close—yet not enmeshed—relationship with his family. (James did.)

4. **How does he describe his last break-up?** This is one of my favorite (somewhat creepy) first date questions because his response is so revealing. If a man blames his ex for their break up or makes it her fault, that's a red flag that he likely doesn't take self-responsibility in relationships. (James took responsibility for his part.)

These are my baseline criteria for choosing to trust a long-term partner. What might your baseline criteria be? What questions could you ask potential partners to discern if they might be trustworthy?

Deciding to Trust, Even with Imperfections

"Trust is the active engagement with the unknown. Trust is risky. It's vulnerable. It's a leap of faith."
—Esther Perel, author of *Mating in Captivity*

While a potential partner can demonstrate trustworthiness, they cannot make you trust them. That is a choice you, and only you, can make. Will you take a risk and open your heart to this person, knowing that you may get hurt? Will you let yourself fall into the uncertainty of love?

When we love, we open ourselves up for pain, disappointment, rejection, pain and heartbreak. Even in the healthiest relationships, there will be painful moments. No matter how ideal and trustworthy your partner is, you will eventually feel pain.

Many women can intuitively sense this truth, and so they keep their heart closed, requiring a partner to continue to prove his love over and over again. Let me tell you a story on this topic...

The Princess, the Knight and the Dragon

Once there was a beautiful princess who lived high on the hill in her castle. One of her knights fell deeply in love with her and asked for her hand in marriage.

She said, "Oh I would love to, but there is just one little thing. There is a dragon that lives over that hill. I can't sleep well at night knowing the dragon is nearby. If you can kill the dragon and bring it's head back to me, I will marry you."

Determined and eager, the knight set out to kill the dragon. The next day he returned with the dragon's head.

The princess smiled and said, "Thank you! But you see, before I marry you, I saw that there is another two-headed dragon on the other hill. Can you kill that one, too?"

255

The knight was a bit frustrated, but he understood. He wanted her to feel safe and secure in her castle, ready to marry him. So he ventured out and killed the two-headed dragon.

He returned with the two heads, offering them to the princess. "Wow, well done!" she said.
He beamed with pride. "Will you marry me now?" he asked.

"I will...but there is just one more thing. There is a three-headed dragon over on that other hill. Will you get it?" she asked. "Then we can have a big wedding to celebrate."

The knight ventured off and never returned. Rumor has it he found a princess in another land that he married and they live happily together.

The original princess sighed sadly. "See, I can never trust men. They always leave."

Debrief

Can you see yourself in this story? Have you ever required a potential partner to "prove" themselves to you over and over again, never quite satisfied? This is common.

Requiring that person to endlessly "prove" themselves creates a dynamic where they cannot win, because they can never do enough to "earn" your trust and respect. In that case, the potential partner will either give up and become resentful, or they will leave and find a more appreciative, trusting woman.

Specific Ways We Distrust Love

Like the princess in the above story, we all have unique ways we refuse to trust love. Our distrust builds walls around our hearts.

Why do we say we want love, yet (often unconsciously) block love?

Because love is both our greatest desire and our greatest fear.

Intimacy is not particularly safe. When you open your heart to love someone and to be loved, hurt, rejection and disappointment are inevitable. You will fight, you will be upset, you will feel pain.

Intimacy is terrifying, absolutely terrifying, to the part of you that wants safety.

To protect ourselves from potential pain, we (unconsciously) develop strategies. These are sneaky little ways we avoid truly opening our hearts to another person. I call these our "protective strategies," which we often learned in childhood to keep ourselves safe, yet they also block intimacy.

Example protective strategies:

- Trying to control others
- Putting on a (fake) happy face
- Judging others
- Agreeing with others to get what you want
- Judging yourself as not good enough
- Denying how you feel
- Suppressing your needs
- Seeking approval
- Complying to avoid confrontation

I have yet to meet any person who doesn't have protective strategies.

Your protective strategies may be different, but it is worthwhile to ask yourself, "What do I do that blocks intimacy?"

If you remember back to Rani from the previous chapter, these were a few of her protective strategies that we worked on together:

- Staying safe by intellectualizing instead of feeling
- Trying to stay in control and in charge of the situation
- Not asking for help or sharing desires
- Refusing to let a partner impact her heart
- Shutting down her sensuality

You can discover your personal protective mechanisms by looking at your past relationships. What was the reason you broke up? What was your part in the breakup? What did YOU do that led to the end of the relationship? (See "Exercise: Discover Your Walls" below)

Once you understand the behaviors you did that contributed to the breakup, with gentle awareness, the next question is: Why did you do these behaviors? What need were you trying to get met?

For example, in one of my breakups, he wanted an open relationship, but I didn't. Yet I agreed to doing an open relationship because I was afraid of losing him and being alone. I didn't trust what I wanted (monogamy). Knowing this helps me have more compassion with myself, and also helps me see warning signs of when I may be tempted to repeat the same protective strategies.

All these protective strategies repeat over and over and over again until we become aware of them.

So the game is not to "get rid of" your protective strategies, but rather to become aware of them. With awareness, you can cultivate compassion and maybe even a little humor. Once you know your protective strategies, you can play a cheeky game of hide-and-seek with your own strategies.

For example, you'll catch yourself doing something you know blocks intimacy like judging your partner, and so in that moment, you can give yourself an internal wink and say, "Hey, I see you. I know you're criticizing him because you're scared of getting close. It's okay." Bringing humor, compassion and playfulness into noticing your protective strategies is a game-changer.

Ultimately, our protective mechanisms want to be loved and accepted. Can we become aware of the ways we block intimacy and embrace them? Can we get curious and compassionate, rather than judgmental, toward our own protective strategies?

Our protective strategies and the specific ways we distrust love will arise again and again, especially in long-term partnership. The trick is to notice them, and in that awareness, make a new choice.

Marissa Trusts Her Husband Again

Marissa came to work with me on her marriage because her husband Joe was an "ignorant workaholic." She explained to me that her husband never came home from work when he said he would, causing her and her kids to wait for hours to eat dinner. He would flop in front of the TV, zoning out. He never did anything romantic for her anymore and he hadn't bought her flowers in goodness knows how long. He knew nothing about her daily life. I could hear the distrust of him and his love dripping from her voice.

"And you?" I asked. "What do you do when this happens?"

"Well, I ignore him. Or criticize him and demand he pay more attention to us," she said.

"Does it work?" I asked.

"No. He just pulls farther and farther away," she said angrily.

This story is all too common, and sad, because it doesn't have to be this way.

Over the next three months, I helped Marissa look at where she had stopped trusting that her husband cared about her, her desires and their family. When had she decided he must not care about her and thereby wasn't worthy of her trust?

She had spent years not expressing her desires or feelings, which had built up a thick crust around her heart. When we don't own and ask vulnerably for our desires, we tend to criticize, nag and ignore our intimate partners. Our criticism veils our deepest wishes.

When our partner receives this criticism or easeless demands, he or she will usually pull away from the relationship, as the knight did above with the princess and as Marissa's husband did with her. Feeling our partner's distance reinforces our belief that we can't trust him with our hearts. It is a vicious cycle of distrust and distance.

Marissa cried during our sessions, sharing her heartbreak about the times he didn't show up for her. I listened and understood, then gently asked her what she was believing about her husband. She was believing:

- That he didn't care.
- That he wasn't invested in their family.
- That he didn't cherish her.

Together we questioned those stories. I asked her how she might behave if she fully trusted that her husband loved her, adored her and cared about their family. She admitted that she'd be softer, kinder, gentler and would ask for what she wanted. So she tried it.

She really wanted a weekly family dinner, so in an openhearted way, she asked her husband if he would come home from work early one night a week to make it happen. He agreed.

She also realized she wanted some undivided attention from him at night. Instead of criticizing him for zoning out, she vulnerably asked if he would join her in the bath that night. Of course, he said yes. They even had sex again!

Over time, her husband noticed how much kinder and more loving his wife had become, and he responded in turn. He showed up more often for the family, was more present during time together, and made an effort to appreciate her more often.

Marissa realized her husband was not the (entire) problem. She saw how her hurt hardened into anger, which led to criticism and contempt, which caused her husband to turn away from her. And when he turned away, she became more hurt and angry. It was a vicious cycle.

The good news is, it only takes one person to change the dance. Relationships are like a tango—sometimes beautiful, sometimes painful—yet always with the behavior of two people. When one person begins dancing to a new tune, the other person must change their steps, as well.

Marissa chose to change her part of the dance. She chose to trust her husband again, to release her hurt, and to show up as the loving, kind woman she really was. And in doing so, her husband began to change, too. She found love in their marriage again.

The feminine gift is to soften the walls around our hearts, to put down our armor and to create an openhearted, vulnerable invitation for the masculine to step into—or not. It is enormously brave to be this soft and inviting, to truly trust in the power of love. Simple to say, hard to do, as the next story illustrates...

Inviting James Into Partnership

After our trip to Australia, I realized: *I want to be in a relationship with this man.* The feeling had been dawning on me for a few weeks now, but the beauty of our time abroad together solidified the desire.

I felt scared admitting that I wanted a committed relationship, because James had said many times that he didn't want to be in a relationship. He was happy being single, thank you very much.

I knew where he stood from the first day we met, and at that time, I didn't want a relationship, either.

And yet, a few months later, my desire had changed. More than anything, I believe in the power of desire, so I knew I had to trust this feeling. It was time to take action.

Unfortunately, my initial communication was less than elegant. In fact, it was a trainwreck.

I passive-aggressively sent him an article called: *Why If You Don't Commit to Her, You're a Coward*, and told him to read it. Annoyed, he asked if I was trying to tell him something.

I made a snarky comment about his lack of commitment to our connection, then I cringed and apologized to him. This is not the gentle, openhearted feminine way of communicating that I preach and practice. Frankly, my fear of rejection was having me communicate like a b*tch.

This moment made me realize I needed to get more vulnerable and honest with my desire. I journaled on the plane what I was looking for, outlining specifically what a "committed relationship" meant to me, so I knew exactly what I was inviting him into.

I wrote down things like..

- We actively lean towards each other
- We stay committed even when it feels challenging
- We live as a team, building a life together
- We may or may not be monogamous, but our commitment to our relationship comes before any other connections
- Etc.

Once my plane landed, I gathered up my courage to try this communication again. First, I texted a couple of girlfriends, letting them know what I was about to do, and asked for support. My girlfriends sent encouraging texts, reminding me of the beauty of my desire. I sent a little prayer to the universe, asking for support in trusting my desire and in trusting love, even if this man was a "no" to my invitation. I also asked the universe to help me communicate lovingly, as an open invitation.

Then, I began recording a voice note to James, pouring out my heart and sharing my desire for commitment with as much vulnerability as I could. My heart thumping loudly, my cheeks were hot and my palms sweaty. I felt so exposed and uncertain.

A few minutes later, he responded. "Wow. Thanks for saying what you want. I'll need to think about it. Give me a few days and I'll get back to you."

I said, "Of course. Take your time."

A part of me wanted to push him to decide right away so I didn't have to feel so nervous, uncertain, and vulnerable. Yet I knew pushing him wouldn't help. So I waited.

While I waited, I worked on trusting love. I reminded myself that the universe will help me find the right life partner, and if that partner wasn't James, it would be someone else amazing. I reminded myself that I can trust my desire, even if the desire doesn't work out exactly how I planned. As they say in twelve-step programs, I practiced, "Letting go and letting God."

A few days later, James called me. My heart was racing when I picked up the phone. He said, "I miss you. Can we go back to talking again like before?"

My heart sank. I missed him too, but I could feel our relationship was at a fork in the road. My intuition told me that we either commit to deeper intimacy, or it was time to move on. If I continued relating casually, as we were, I would be denying and distrusting my own knowing, which would eventually lead to me becoming resentful of him.

I responded, "No, I can't do that. I'd like a clear decision on what you want to do."

He said he needed to think more and hung up.

About thirty minutes later, he called back and said, "I'm scared, but I'm in."

I felt so touched, soft, scared, excited and nervous about being in a relationship with him.

He told me later this was the first time he'd consciously chosen to commit to a woman. In every other relationship he had ended up in, as a natural next step, but he always had one foot in, one foot out the door. My clearly-stated desire and open invitation gave him a chance to pause and truly reflect on if he wanted this partnership as a deliberate choice. As it turns out, he did.

From that day on, the way James related to me was completely different. He showed up, both feet in, actively engaged and ready. I was a bit unprepared for how involved and committed he would be to me, to us and to what we're creating together, but I loved it.

———————

I share that story as an example of how differently I showed up when I didn't trust myself, my desire, or our connection (as in sending the passive aggressive article) vs. when I took the time to build a foundation of trust in myself, our connection and the universe.

Frankly, when I am not trusting, I become controlling, bitchy and passive aggressive. My trust is the key ingredient that allows me to soften and become an open invitation for the masculine. My trust invites out his brilliance.

> *The bigger you can trust, the bigger you can love.*

Your trust does, too. Trusting your partner, of course, but ultimately, the bigger invitation to trust is much deeper than that. Can you trust your desires, your intuition, your knowing? Can you trust love? Can you trust the universe or God?

The bigger you can trust, the bigger you can love.

Exercise: Discover the Walls Around Your Heart

Each of us have specific ways we distrust love. We can discover our unique "protective strategies" by reflecting on our past.

This may be the last exercise you want to do, but I promise you, the rewards are immense. The self-awareness you receive from this level of introspection can save you years of heartbreak.

The instructions:

1. Review your previous break ups or heartbreaking experiences. Choose one particularly vivid heart-breaking experience to work with. You can always do other situations later once you understand the process.

2. What led to the end of the relationship? Write out a few sentences on the story at the top of your page.

3. Next, list the behaviors you did that contributed to the breakup. Be specific here. Example: I denied how I felt, I judged him, I tried to control him, I avoided his questions, etc. Focus specifically on YOUR behavior and actions. Even if you are sure the breakup was your ex's fault, there are likely ways you showed up imperfectly, as well.

4. Next to each behavior, elaborate on your motivations. Why did you do that behavior? What were you trying to accomplish? Ex: "I judged him as an attempt to feel superior, and thereby safer," or, "I denied how I felt so that I didn't risk losing him."

5. Lastly, what do you need to feel safe enough in love? Ex: "I need to know that he is fully committed to building a life with me," or, "I need to know that he loves me, even in my imperfections."

We're never totally safe, but we're often the worst version of ourselves when we feel unsafe, as if we need to protect ourselves. Knowing what will help you feel safe enough is an important place to start in building a secure relationship.

Calibrating Your Trusting

In this chapter, we looked at trust as both an observation and a decision. First, we need to discern if this person is worthy of our trust, and then we need to actively decide to trust, despite imperfections.

Consider: Do you trust too easily? Or not easily enough?

If you trust too easily, you likely find yourself in dysfunctional relationships with unsteady, unreliable partners. You may make excuses for their behavior, but ultimately, you can tell this person isn't right for you. *(If this is you, see exercise on "discerning trustworthiness" below.)*

If you don't trust easily enough, you likely are either still single or are with partners upon whom you don't rely. You may operate like independent beings living parallel lives, even in a relationship. You know your heart is not as open as it could be, and you feel a bit guarded. *(If this is you, see exercise on "choosing to trust" below.)*

Exercise: Discerning Trustworthiness

If you trust too easily, practice cultivating your "inner father." This is the part of you that asks the challenging questions to understand a potential partner's character. Your "inner father" will help you discern and think logically before giving away your whole heart. Here's how it works:

1. Write out your past relationships. Which of your partner's characteristics frustrated you or caused pain?

    Maybe it was the constant ups and downs, financial insecurity, possessive jealousy, etc.

2. Create a series of questions you might ask to discover if someone you date has these characteristics. See the four questions above that I used to discern if James would be a good partner for me. Your questions may be different because your values are likely different. Aim for three-to-five core questions.

3. These questions are your "Checkpoint" questions, the kind your inner father would ask when you bring someone home, in order to better understand their character. These questions serve as a gatekeeper to your heart and body.

4. Next time you go on a date, and ideally before you have sex with that person (because sex can flood you with bonding hormones), ask these questions. Observe your date's responses.

5. Go slowly and listen to your intuition. Do you feel a full body *yes*? Do you feel a hesitant *yes*, like you may need more info? Or do you feel a *no*?

    Even if you don't understand WHY your body is a *yes* or a *no*, you can trust your body's intuitive wisdom (see Chapter 3 for more info).

6. If you trust too easily, you may rush into partnership. The antidote is to slooooooow down. Aim for one or two dates a week at most so you have time to digest the experiences, stay connected to yourself and listen to your intuition.

Exercise: Choosing to Trust

If you don't trust easily, you need to cultivate your "inner romantic," the part of you that longs for lifelong fairytale love (even if that concept makes you cringe with cheesiness). Embrace the uncertainty of love, knowing you will get hurt, but that you are resilient and true love is worth the risk. Let yourself long for love, yearn for a partner and open your heart.

Here's how:

1. Next time you are on a date (either with someone new or your current partner), imagine the person in front of you is the most brilliant human on earth. Find all of their powerful qualities.

2. When your brain starts judging that person or finding reasons why he or she is not trustworthy or good enough, just notice those thoughts and let them go. Come back to their great qualities.

3. Soften your body—especially your chest, belly and pussy. These are often places where we are tight and guarded, holding habitual tension and physical armoring. See if you can slightly relax these areas.

4. Ask this person to help you with something. You could ask their opinion on a business dilemma, ask for their help finding directions or ask their perspective on a challenge. Listen to the answer and look for the gold in it.

5. Share something you appreciate about this person. What do you already love about them? Let them know. This act of loving helps you further open your heart.

Each of these steps will help you soften and open just a little bit to allow more love in. It will help you focus on this person's great qualities and gently open into trusting this person more fully.

Invitation: Grab Your Journal

1. How well do you trust the masculine? Too easily, too challenging or just right?

2. How can you "calibrate" your level of trust so you're both discerning AND open? (See exercises above.)

3. What protective strategies do you use to protect yourself from intimacy when you get scared? What situations trigger these protective strategies?

4. Look at your communication with current or previous partners. Are you communicating trust or distrust through your words and actions?

5. What would it be like to fully trust the masculine? How would your behavior change?

6. What would it be like to fully trust yourself, your love and the universe?

CHAPTER 13

SEX

Having amazing sex requires every concept we've learned so far. The foundation of great sex is knowing your pussy, knowing how to feel pleasure in your body, knowing your desires and being able to communicate them. Understanding masculine and feminine and learning to dance with both energies is what creates sexual tension. And trusting men (or whomever your partner is) is a prerequisite to ecstatic intimacy.

So here we are—sex.

Sex can be so, so much more than what we see in ads, media, porn and movies. It can be ecstatic, intimate, deep, profound, spiritual, wild...and more. Our capacity for sex is as varied as our capacity for personal expression.

Yet, for many of us, to have sex like this, we have to unlearn painful messages and social conditioning around sex. Let me tell you my story...

My Sexual Explorations

I grew up fascinated yet at the same time afraid of the power of sex.

I learned early on that sex was dirty and disgusting. In my public high school, my only sex education was images of herpes

271

and crabs, statistics on AIDS deaths and a stern talk about the importance of remaining "pure" and abstinent until marriage. Seriously—this was in the early 2000s!

Despite the (lack of) education, I felt drawn toward sexuality, as if I intuitively knew there was something powerful and magical about it.

When I was thirteen, my boyfriend and I shared our first kiss on the dance floor at his bar mitzvah (mazel tov!). I remember feeling so alive, so myself, and so wildly in love with the feeling of kissing.

My early erotic experiences made me feel so lit up that I wondered how sexuality could be a bad thing. How could something so pleasurable and connected be sinful?

I felt so intrigued by relationships and sexuality that when I was fourteen years old, I opened an online teen advice column. Young people would write in with their love life dilemmas and I would give them advice on what to do, foreshadowing my later career as an intimacy coach.

As a young adult, sexuality was a major part of my personal growth journey, a core way to discover who I was. I've wondered, "What can I learn about myself and about life through sexuality? Where are my edges and my taboos? How can I consciously lean into those edges and see who I am on the other side?"

In my sexual journey, I went from only having sex with committed, monogamous boyfriends I loved...to one night stands and "free love" sexuality...to open relating and polyamory...to group experiences, temple nights, and threesomes...and now back to committed, monogamous sex with my partner.

What a wild journey! Along the way I faced many fears ("What if I accidentally get pregnant or get an STI?"—FYI, I didn't get either), doubts ("If I kiss a woman, does that make me bi?"), and shame ("Will I be less 'marriageable' because of all of these sexual experiences?").

Each time, I had to work with my mind to "unlearn" what I had been culturally taught about sexuality. What most surprised me was how natural, normal and connecting most of my experiences were. How freeing it could be to try something new sexually in a conscious, connected way. Maybe sex wasn't the scary, shameful thing I was taught.

Before we dive into the beautiful possibilities for YOUR erotic life, let's rewind and explore what makes sexuality so taboo, so dark and so shame-ridden.

Why We're Challenged by Sexuality

Remember my disastrous experience with sexual education? Maybe you had a similar experience. Or you had parents that never talked about sexuality, or worse yet, they shamed sex. Or you grew up in a conservative religion that portrayed sex as sinful and dirty.

No matter our background, we can hardly escape the sex-negative messages in our culture—from parents, from schooling, from religion, from the media. Unless you've deliberately worked on and questioned your sexual beliefs, you likely carry cultural shame and stigma in this area of your life.

Let's put these messages into historical context. For thousands of years, a woman who admitted she loved sex and had lots of sex would be at best, the town slut...and at worst, damaged goods, unfit to marry, or she may even have been killed. In some parts of the world, this is still the case.

With this context, it is no wonder many women struggle to know themselves sexually.

Then there's trauma. Globally, an estimated 736 million women— almost one in three—have been subjected to intimate partner violence, non-partner sexual violence or both at least once in their lives (UNWomen.Org, 2021).

These are insane, heartbreaking statistics. Can you imagine the imprint this collective trauma leaves on the female psyche? How unsafe she may feel in her own body?

If you are reading this chapter with fear, trepidation or uncertainty, I want you to know you are not alone, and you can heal from this. You can learn to love sex again. It may be a long journey, and may require professional support, but it is possible.

Even if you've never experienced sexual trauma, you may still feel as if it is not safe to talk about or explore your sexuality. This silence, shame and secrecy about sex leads to mediocre sex at best or traumatizing sex at worst. No wonder so many people struggle sexually!

Here are some of the sexual challenges I hear from my clients:

- Feeling like sex is mechanical and boring, with the same moves over and over
- Being checked out or in your head during sex, unable to feel pleasure in your body
- Only feeling comfortable having sex when you're drunk, high or numb
- Unable to orgasm, or struggling to consistently orgasm
- Feeling uncomfortable communicating what you want
- Wanting more sex than your partner and feeling embarassed or rejected
- Wanting less sex than your partner, and possibly "doing it for them" or as a chore
- Being "too busy" for sex, not enough time
- Not enjoying the way your partner touches you
- Penetration causes physical and/or emotional pain
- Struggling to find a sexual partner you trust
- Painfully reliving past traumas during sexual experiences

Can you relate to any of these challenges?

They are so, so normal. And unfortunately, because of our sex-negative culture, many people don't get the support they need to move through these issues.

Even if your sex is good, maybe you wonder if it could even be better. What else is there to explore?

Sex is a skill, and like any skill, we can practice sex and get better at it. We can learn from experienced people, we can talk about sex, ask questions, and discover tools and techniques. We don't have to "fuck in the dark."

What's possible when we approach sex as a skill, something to learn and cultivate?

We become curious and exploratory again, instead of putting pressure on ourselves.
We laugh off "failed attempts" as part of the learning journey instead of as a point of shame.
We ask questions, share our desires and ask our partners what they want, instead of expecting ourselves or others to be mind readers.
We feel free to explore our pleasure instead of feeling broken or wrong.

When we treat sex as a skill or an art, we discover a whole world of openness and curiosity.

This chapter will give you stories and information on how to move beyond sexual challenges and toward more epic lovemaking.

> *When we treat sex as a skill or an art, we discover a whole world of openness and curiosity.*

Why are you having sex?

The first question to ask when exploring your sexuality is, "Why are you having sex?"

This is not a rhetorical question. I really mean this—ponder it for a second.

There are a thousand reason to have sex. Here are a few I've heard:

- To relieve stress
- To make my partner like me
- To feel close emotionally
- To touch God
- To get out of my head
- To experience pleasure
- To return to my essence
- To sustain our relationship
- To loosen up and have fun

What's your reason?

Knowing your motivation for why you're having sex will influence the type of sex you have, and also the advice I'll give to help you have "better" sex. Because what is "better" to one person may sound horrible to another, as they are having sex for different purposes.

Depending on your motivation for having sex, you may be curious to explore one of the three levels of sex in more depth. Let me explain...

The Three Levels of Sex

There are three basic levels in which you can have sex.

The first level is **purely physical**—how do we create physical pleasure? What types of touch and sensations can we explore? How can we discover different types of orgasms? This level is particularly important if you struggle to feel pleasure.

The next level is the **emotional level**. How do you explore the emotional texture of the moment? Can you turn on rage, play with greed, experiment with the seduction of grief? How do you express love and deeply connect through sex? Bringing emotions into sex creates new flavors for your eroticism and adds dimension.

The final level is the **spiritual level**. How do you worship your partner through the act of lovemaking? How do you feel connected to God or spirit when in orgasm? What is the sacred purpose of your union? Will you let yourself be worshipped as a goddess? Can you find the profound nature of a profane moment?

These levels are not linear, meaning you do not "progress" from one to the next. Rather, these levels are more like cooking with spices—each adds more complexity, depth, nuance and magic into your erotic experiences. Let's explore each level further...

The Physical Level of Great Sex

The physical level of sex is about discovering and expanding your capacity for **pleasure** and **sensation**. This can be challenging for many people, as it was for my client, Amira.

Amira Has an Orgasm

When I began working with Amira, a young woman in her mid-twenties, she felt deep shame because she had never had an orgasm. She enjoyed sex with her boyfriend, but wondered what was wrong with her that she couldn't orgasm.

During our work together, we explored the cultural and physical reasons for this. Culturally, she had grown up in a religiously conservative household that treated sex as sinful, so each time she had sex, she felt a tinge of shame, which understandably made it difficult to relax into the pleasure.

We also discussed how she puts enormous pressure on herself to "perform" in all areas of her life. She was a top student and now a budding business leader. She always had a "goal" to accomplish. When it came to sex, she had high expectations on her body to become turned on quickly and easily and pressured herself to orgasm. Her boyfriend's eager hope for her to climax didn't help.

I encouraged her to let go of the goal of climaxing entirely, and instead, focus on feeling sensation and pleasure in her body. Often having a sexual "goal" is counterproductive for women, as female orgasms tend to happen most easily when you're relaxed and surrendered.

Then, to help her feel more pleasure, I recommended she do the following:

1. Share her desires openly.

I encouraged her to share desires and boundaries more freely with her partner by asking each other questions like, "What do you want this experience to be like? Is there anything you definitely don't want to happen?" She told her partner she wanted to take their intimacy slower, spending more time on foreplay without the pressure to get quickly turned on. This open communication helped her feel safe and more connected to him.

2. Breathe deeply and fully.

She noticed that, like many women, she tends to breathe shallowly due to stress and tension. So, we worked on practicing deep breaths, like the Deep Pussy Breath from Chapter 5. This helped her body open, which allowed her to feel more sensations.

3. Add movement.

She shared that she feels shy sexually, and her body tends to freeze as she gets aroused. So, I invited her to bring gentle movement into her body during foreplay, such as swaying her hips, wiggling her toes, and undulating her spine. This helped her loosen up stuck tension in her body and allowed her erotic energy to flow more freely.

4. Make sounds.

Like many women, Amira felt embarrassed by the sounds her body wanted to make, so she stayed silent throughout the sexual experience. I taught her how the throat and the pussy are intrinsically linked, which means when she opens her throat, she helps her pussy open as well. She practiced allowing sounds to emerge from her while having sex—soft sighs, gentle moans, and deep "ahhhh"'s. At first, she felt awkward doing this, but she quickly noticed how making sounds opened her body and allowed her to feel increased sensations.

5. Soften.

I showed Amira the feminine energetic channel that runs up the front of the body, connecting the pussy, the womb, the belly, the heart, and the throat. I let her know that penetration can feel more connected and heartfelt when we soften this channel fully. She started noticing habitual tension there and invited (not forced) her body to soften throughout the day and especially during lovemaking.

My invitation—practice right now, as you're reading this, to bring awareness to this central channel of your body and invite it to soften.

6. Accept.

Finally, I encouraged her to accept herself and her body, as it is today, letting go of any goals or hopes of how she "should be." This is a difficult one! Yet cultivating acceptance for ourselves and for our sex as it is creates space for us to be surprised and delighted by what might unfold next.

These six practices allowed her to feel more comfortable in her body. She began experiencing far more pleasure than before, particularly as she slowed down their lovemaking. Eventually, while orgasm was no longer the goal, she did have an orgasm with her partner. She sent me an ecstatic text after the experience about how much she is loving sex now. Very cool!

You can take on these six practices, as well. They are a powerful roadmap to experiencing more physical sensation and pleasure in sex. Let's dive into tip #1 now—sharing your desires openly—as this can be quite difficult for many women.

Knowing What You Want

"I don't really like sex," my client tells me, looking down and twisting her skirt into knots.

"Hmm ... do you not like sex, or do you not like the sex you're having?" I ask.

"I don't like the sex I'm having. It feels rushed and abrasive, and honestly, I don't feel much pleasure," she responds.

I nod and ask, "Well, what *does* turn you on?"

"I guess I don't know," she replies.

And that is where our work together begins.

See, a lot of us were sold a type of sex that is fast, direct, genital-to-genital, straight-to-it. That's what porn shows (which is most people's default sex education). Unfortunately, it's often not the kind of sex most women enjoy.

Or as my former teacher, **Nicole Daedone** said in her book *Slow Sex*—"Women love sex. Just not what is on the menu."

In the absence of other options, a woman will decide SHE is the problem in her sex life.

- "I must not like sex enough."

- "I guess I am not a turned on woman."
- "I don't orgasm so sometimes I fake it."
- "Maybe I should see a doctor about my low libido..."

Here is what I think....

There is nothing wrong with you. Your sex and your desire is perfect, just waiting for the right invitation to emerge—YOUR invitation. Your sex is waiting for you to take the reigns and learn what you like.

You don't have to settle for mediocre sex. You don't have to resign to "doing it for him." You can learn what genuinely lights your body up, what your pussy craves.You can explore your unique "erotic language" and show your partner(s).

You're not broken—you're a woman awakening to her inherent eroticism.

So, let's begin with the question—*What turns you on? What do you enjoy sexually?*

Maybe you have a whole list of your favorite ways to get turned on, or maybe you've never explored this before. Either way, your erotic desire is ever-evolving and expanding, so it helps to keep coming back to this question time and time again.

How do you discover what you want?

- Notice what feels good—and what doesn't—during your erotic experiences.
- Experiment with ways of touching yourself through self-pleasure (see Chapter 6).
- Read books on erotic techniques to get new ideas.
- Let yourself fantasize.

Let's talk about fantasy for a minute. Fantasy plays a powerful role in the journey to reclaim your sexuality. By bringing your imagination into the erotic space, you can discover a whole host of turn ons you didn't know you had.

Often women avoid fantasizing as something that is dirty or wrong, especially if you're in a monogamous relationship.

If that's you, will you write yourself a permission slip to try fantasizing?

Letting your mind drift into novel sexual scenarios is an excellent way to discover what turns you on, feel more sexual, and invent new things to explore with a partner (or alone!).

If you're not sure where to start with fantasy, consider:

- What sexy moments have you read in books or seen on TV that might be fun to try? (Fifty Shades of Gray, anyone?)
- What dreams have you had that left your body buzzing?

If no fantasy comes to mind yet, try this—begin self-pleasuring, gently, slowly. As you touch yourself, allow your mind to drift and any images to form. What pops in your head? Welcome any images, no matter how taboo or weird they seem.

Inside of our erotic fantasies, there is often hidden wisdom. We may discover our deeper life desires tucked away in a seemingly weird sexual fantasy.

For example, if you fantasize about being raped and taken by force (as many women secretly do), the deeper desire underneath may be to be ravished and to let go fully into surrender. You may discover that you long to release your controlling exterior and fully trust life. That's good information, is it not?

Lastly, it helps to know the unique way you get turned on, or your "desire style," especially if you struggle with not often feeling "in the mood." I learned these styles from the highly informative book, *Come as You Are* by **Emily Nagoski**.

There are two basic types of desire styles:

1. **Spontaneous arousal**, which is more common in men (75%) but is also present in about 15% of women, means the desire to have sex comes up suddenly and strongly. The impulse to engage intimately appears first, then you may take action on it.

2. **Responsive arousal**, which is more common in women, means that sexual stimuli must already be present to want sex. This means you may need touching, foreplay, kissing, watching a sexy scene, etc. **first**, and then your body's enjoyment of that stimulation may inspire your desire for sex.

If you recognize yourself as "responsive arousal" (I am too), then you may need to deliberately create sexy situations before you feel turned on. For example, you could go up and passionately kiss your partner and see how that feels. Or do a sensual dance and dress in lingerie to see if that helps you feel more "in the mood." Or ask your partner to stroke your belly and thighs and notice how your body feels.

Moral of the story—no matter what your relationship is to your sexual desire, I promise your desire is still there waiting to be discovered, explored and honored.

Then once you find your sexual desire, how do you communicate it?

Communicating What You Want

Communicating our desires may be challenging or awkward! But it is so important.

An easy way to start the conversation is by sharing appreciation of what you love. "I love when you kiss me gently." "I love when you pull my hair." "I love your caresses." Etc.

Sharing what you are already enjoying can be easier both to say and receive than sharing what you don't like.

When women feel uncomfortable sharing their sexual desires, they may instead turn to criticism, such as, "You're going too fast!" "Stop touching me so roughly!" Or, "I don't like the way you kiss." This tends to cause their partners to shut down, pull away and feel inadequate. It's a lose-lose conversation inside an already delicate, emotional topic.

A few prompts you can use to get a win-win conversation going instead:

- "I love it when you..."
- "It turns me on when we..."
- "It feels so good when..."
- "I'd love having more ___ in our sex."
- "Would you ___ next time we're intimate?"
- "What do you want more of?"
- "How can I be a better lover to you?"

Let Your Body Talk—Honestly

If you're having a hard time communicating with words, know that your body is always communicating. Even if you're not explicitly telling your partner what you want, the sounds you're making, your facial expressions, your body language...all of this is communicating to your partner whether they're on track and bringing you pleasure or if they're off track and may need to course correct.

In both verbal and nonverbal sexual communication, honesty is key. Are you giving your partner honest signals about what feels good and what doesn't?

I cannot tell you how many women I've talked to who admit that they exaggerate how good a partner's touch feels, fake an orgasm or pretend to enjoy sex more than they do. I get why—it can be difficult to communicate honestly when something isn't working for you.

Yet, "exaggerating" or outright lying, either through your words or through your body signals, does both you and your partner an enormous disservice.

Imagine your partner is trying to learn to play the guitar of your body. Meanwhile, the guitar is lying. Your partner goes to play a chord and the guitar plays a totally different chord. Without accurate feedback on the "notes" your partner is playing, it would be quite difficult to learn to play the guitar, right?

It's the same with your body. When you misrepresent how something feels, your partner doesn't get the information they need to learn to play the "notes" of your body. They don't have a chance to get more skilled at bringing you pleasure.

This is why it is so important to communicate honestly, verbally and nonverbally, through your face, body and sound about what is genuinely bringing pleasure and what isn't.

The Emotional Level of Sex

Beyond the physical level of sex lies the EMOTIONAL level of sex. This level is about the connection between you and your intimate partner(s), how you feel emotionally about the experiences you're having and the feelings you're bringing into your erotic experiences.

Howard and Jenna

Howard reached out to James and me for support, because he and Jenna, his wife of seven years, had stopped having sex. Their first baby was a year old, which had thrown a wrench in their sex life. While their intimacy had never been amazing, it was now nonexistent.

They were bickering more than usual and felt the trust had broken down. Howard felt sexually frustrated, while Jenna felt pressured to have sex she wasn't interested in. He felt ignored, as if she was paying more attention to their baby than to him.

They flew to Bali to do a one-week private intensive with James and me on their sex life.

The first thing we worked on was clearing out old resentments and hurt places.

Often when a couple sexually pulls apart, it's because they have pulled apart emotionally.

> *Often when a couple sexually pulls apart, it's because they have pulled apart emotionally.*

We spent the first day acknowledging and honoring each of their hurt places. Within the hour, they were in tears, sharing and releasing old stuck pain. The day ended with a long hug. Howard said, "If we only got today's session from the week, the whole investment was worth it."

After emptying out stuck hurts, we moved on to understanding turn ons. We gave them a prompt, "It turns me on when you ..." and let them share back and forth. They were surprised by some of each other's responses and were inspired to try new things.

Jenna wanted foreplay that lasted all day, with teasing touch and flirtation throughout the day, culminating in a sexy experience. Howard was often too tired at night but loved afternoon or morning sex. This information gave each of them the knowledge they needed to turn each other on—the when, how and the what.

Next, we worked on masculine/feminine dynamics, and particularly how to use polarity to create in-the-moment sexiness. They ran a business together, lived together, were raising a child together and more. In all that togetherness, they found themselves depolarized, like best buddies (see Chapter 12), so we designed specific "transition rituals" when work ended before lover time began where they could consciously move into either masculine or feminine energy. This helped them see each other as lovers again.

Jenna and I worked on how to communicate her tender desires to Howard, while Howard and James worked on how to receive the feminine's desires openly and graciously. This helped Jenna feel safe to express herself more fully. The men also worked on tantric techniques for non-ejaculation so he could last longer, giving her body more time to fully open.

The week was a phenomenal success. Over the course of the week, they had the best sex of their relationship, they cleared hurt spots and left feeling turned on and lit up. They said that seeing their growth as a couple this week gave them renewed hope for their future together. Seeing the profound transformation Howard and Jenna made was one of the best moments of my career.

Letting Your Heart Be Involved

In the above story, Howard and Jenna needed support not so much on the physical level of sex, but more so on the emotional level, particularly on how their sex life related to their connection.

You may have noticed that it can be difficult to open physically to our partners if our hearts are hurt. If we feel ignored, unwanted, betrayed or hurt, our hearts and pussies may simultaneously close down to our partners.

When you're having sex on purely a physical level, you may be able to only focus on pleasure and not have your heart be involved. But if you want to deepen your erotic experiences, you will have to open your heart, which can feel incredibly vulnerable and exposed.

Deeply intimate sex can be an emotional experience. You may cry, feel unexpected rage or giggle hysterically. Will you give yourself permission to feel emotions during the erotic experience?

Emotions add color and texture to an erotic experience.

For example...

- If you've ever had angry "make up sex," you may have enjoyed how the heat of your anger turned up the fire on the experience.

- Or if you've had "break up sex," you may have noticed how grief broke your heart open and allowed a raw level of intimacy with you and your new ex-lover.

- Or if you've celebrated great news (such as a promotion) with ecstatic lovemaking, you may feel how joy can add buoyancy and vibrancy to intimacy.

In all these experiences, the common denominator is an intense emotion that adds texture and heart into the physical experience of sex.

You can make love with any emotion present in you. Jealousy? Rage? Disgust? Longing? Love? Playfulness? Sadness? All of these emotions can be sexy when moved through your heart and body as you become intimate with your partner(s).

Remember how in Chapter 9, we explored "Swamping," or moving our emotions through our body while finding the turn on and eroticism inside those emotions? That skill applies here in your sex life. Whatever you're feeling can be "fuel for the fire" of your sex.

Imagine you want to bring in the emotion of "love" during sex. How? Softening your body, breathing deeply and moving more slowly during sex will help you access your heart more. During lovemaking, you can also bring to mind a feeling of love or tenderness for your partner, letting their touch ripple not just across your physical body but across your emotional body, as well.

During the act of penetration, you may also imagine opening your body from your pussy up to your heart, as if whatever is penetrating you (fingers, cocks, toys, etc.) can touch all the way up the center of your body. Don't be surprised if this feels unexpectedly vulnerable and you instinctually tighten up against that vulnerability. Continue to invite softness into your body.

The main ingredients of the emotional level of sex are:

1. Feeling connected to your partner. This means clearing any hurt places, resements or stuck spots before engaging sexually together.

2. Allowing your emotions to flow freely in the bedroom. Rage, grief, disgust, joy—play with whatever emotional texture you're currently feeling, adding an erotic edge to it.

3. Softening your body as you make love. Allowing the touch of your partner to penetrate all the way to your heart, feeling the soft tissues around your heart melt.

4. Remembering a sense of love as you "make love." Gaze adoringly at your partner. Look into their eyes. Allow any natural tenderness to emerge.

Navigating the emotional dynamics of connected, heartfelt sex can bring up a number of questions, especially around partnership. Below I respond to a few....

What if you and your partner are different sexually?

Having different turn ons is normal. Have you heard of the five love languages? It's common for couples to have different love languages, but with this knowledge, you can learn to "speak" each other's love languages. It is the same sexually. This presents you with a chance to generously "gift" each other the sexual experiences the other person wants.

For example, if you're dating someone who enjoys kinky activities like spanking, BDSM and being tied up, yet you prefer more smooth jazz and slow massage...you can learn about each other's erotic language. You can be curious to explore kink and see if maybe there's something there that might turn you on. Your partner (hopefully) can get to know how to massage you and create a sensual space that turns you on. The key to this working is willingness and generosity.

I highly recommend *Jaiya's Erotic Blueprints Quiz*, which you can find online, as a way to start the conversation around erotic differences. I encourage all my clients to take it and share their results with their partner(s).

What if I want LESS sex than my partner?

Like Amira's story above, we sometimes put so much pressure on ourselves to "be sexy" or to please a partner erotically, that all this pressure tends to dampen the tender spark of our desire.

The best way to rediscover your desire is to ask your pussy, "Right now, what would make me feel most sexy and alive?" Give your desire space to breathe and come out. Then, act on the desires.

A few practical places to consider if you feel like you have a low libido:

- **Are you sleeping enough?** Sleep deprivation is a sure killer of turn on.
- **Are you moving your body?** We live in a brain-on-a-stick culture. Sensual movement like dance or yoga can help you get in your body and open to your bodily sensations.
- **Are you honest with your partner?** Did your feelings get hurt anywhere? Often, if our feelings got hurt and we didn't clear that, we may shut down sexually.
- **Are you stressed?** Stress activates your fight-or-flight response which can kill your sex drive. Meditate, take deep breaths, have a bath and find ways to calm your nervous system. Then see if sex sounds more appealing.
- **Do you like the way you're being touched?** Often, if you don't like the type of sex you're having, your libido will shut down. This can be an invitation to explore different types of touch and eroticism (see the "This or That" exercise at the end of this chapter).

Consider these questions around your libido:

1. Do I think I have a high, medium, or low libido?
2. How do I FEEL about my libido?

The way you FEEL about your libido is actually more important than what your libido is. If you feel ashamed, embarrassed or guilty for your level of sexual desire, it will cause disconnect in your relationship.

If instead, you can find a place of acceptance for yourself and your level of sexual desire, as well as open curiosity to learn more, that can help you (and your partner) feel more connected as you explore how to match your desires better.

Lastly, remember the two "desire styles?" You may have a responsive desire, which means you don't feel "in the mood" until something sexy is already occurring. If that's true for you, how can you deliberately create a sexy context for yourself? What would you do to intentionally turn yourself on?

Finally, this is an area on which I coach many women, so if you want more personalized support, please do reach out. You can contact me via my website: **www.megandlambert.com**

What if I want MORE sex than my partner?

If you're the partner who wants more sex, you may worry that you're "too much" or something is wrong with you for having a big sexual appetite. You may take your partner's lower libido personally and feel unwanted as a result. You may feel sexually frustrated and resentful. This is normal!

A couple things to consider here:

1. **Your partner's libido doesn't necessarily have anything to do with you.** Your partner may be uninterested in sex due to stress, hormones, diet, body insecurities, overwhelm or just plain being focused on other priorities.

Keeping this in mind can help ward off feelings of being unwanted.

2. **What does sex mean to you?** Sex can represent everything from emotional closeness to basic pressure relief after a long day of work. Back to the question with which we started this chapter—why do you want sex? Are there any deeper needs here, such as wanting to feel reassured that the relationship is doing well? Understanding your needs gives you flexibility in how to get those needs met. For example, if you have sex to feel emotionally close to your partner, in what other ways could you feel that emotional closeness?

3. **You can be creative with your eroticism.** Even if your partner doesn't want as much sex as you do, you can still cultivate your own erotic life. You can self-pleasure, learn sensual dance, write erotica, etc. If you're in an open relationship, you can find outside lovers to meet your sexual desires. Bottom line: You have flexibility and choice in where to channel your erotic energy.

The Spiritual Level of Sex

Once you've explored the physical and emotional levels of sex, consider what might be possible in the spiritual level of sex.

You can have sex to touch the divine, to merge ecstatically with another human, to discover the secret pulse of the universe.

Sex can be a devotional act, an intimate communion between us and God through the realm of another person. As we open to this other person, open to let them touch us, to move us, to be taken by this person ... we can let ourselves be taken and moved by God.

This may feel sacrilegious at first. For many of us growing up in traditional religions, we may have learned that sex is dirty, sinful and "base." Yet I invite you to consider that God wants you to have pleasure. That your body was born for bliss. That your eroticism is your divine birthright. That you can feel connected to spirituality through your sex. At least, try it on for size :)

In a way, sex can become a blueprint for surrender. A template of: What does it feel like to be moved? To be touched? To let go? To be taken by God, by life?

Deep sex, profound sex, mystical sex, animal sex, requires a shedding off of our brain, a surrendering with each breath. We let ourselves go. We let ourselves release into the deep void, the mystery, where neither you, nor I, know what will happen next. Where we're constantly listening, surprised, like two surfers waiting for the wave.

Let the pauses be pregnant and still. When the wave comes, we catch it with our full gusto, letting nothing stop us, holding nothing back, merging into ecstatic union and then letting that crest and go back into stillness. Again and again and again. Listening.

The waves of the ocean and the thrust of sex teaches us about the inhale and the exhale of life. Everything comes and everything goes. We trust the rhythms and the flow and the ebb and the go. We are with life, with ourselves.

Big Pussy, Small Pussy

In Buddhism, they have a term: *big mind, small mind*.

Small mind is your ego, your separate self, your distinct individual identity.
Big mind is the connection with all of the universe, the collective field and that which can hold your small mind.

Well, I believe there's also big pussy and small pussy. Are you connecting with the small pussy of your own body, your own separate self? Your fears, your limitations, your doubts? Your small desires?

Or are you connecting with the big pussy?

Big pussy opens and lets herself devour life.
Cocks, fingers, mouth, labias, tongues.
Envelops everything.
Wants and sucks and slurps and tastes.
Relishing all of humanity.

Are your sex and your lovemaking with small pussy or big pussy?

Sex is the physical embodiment of how a woman can receive all of life. Big pussy is in approval of life. She says *yes*, she takes it all in through her pussy, into her womb, her belly, her heart. We take life into us, let it consume us, and in the heat of sex, we are remade.

When a woman listens to big pussy, she can feel the deeper rhythms of life. The crests, the waves, the pauses. Big pussy is like an ocean or the moon...she has a rhythm. In that way, having sex with big pussy requires listening.

Can she listen devotionally to big pussy? Her partner accesses the divine through her access to the big pussy. By listening actively to big pussy, by hearing the larger waves and rhythms of love-making, she can guide her partner to be brilliant in bed with her. She can show her partner how to open her more fully.

You can feel big pussy right now. Try this: Relax your shoulders. Soften your breath. Take in the surroundings. Bring attention to your pussy and consciously imagine opening your pussy to this moment. What do you notice?

As you open your body and more fully receive this moment, you tap into something deeper, more profound, more divine.

It is not enough to know God. You have to know what gets in the way of God.

It is not enough to know God. You have to know what gets in the way of God.

294

It is not enough to know surrendered, sacred, devotional, primal sex. You have to know what gets in the way of regularly having that kind of sex.

You have to know your own landscape and all of the ways you habitually hold tension and tightness, and "No, I will not open," and all the ways that your fear holds itself in your body, as well as your traumas and your unexpressed emotions.

That longing you feel for deep, sacred sex is real. That fluid longing is the water that will search out your internal dams and break them open until every ounce of your erotic can run free.

The most important work you do in this lifetime is to feel for your own dams. "Where is the flow stuck? Where am I not letting God and sex and myself run through? Where am I holding tight from conditioning, fear and trauma? How can I be loving with the holding? How can I trust in big pussy even more?"

Water doesn't immediately push down dams, but bit, by bit, by bit, water carves through blockages until the water can run free. Your erotic energy is the same. Noticing where your Eros gets blocked and held by stuck emotions, past trauma, and fear is an important step. By slowly bringing your attention and love to these stuck spots, you can breathe, soften and open them so the water of your eroticism can run free.

What do you most identify with?

The free flow of your erotic, divine, esssential self?
Or the dams, constrictions, fears and blockages?

Your ego wants to create an identity, a tightness, *this is who I am* versus being with the flow of the erotic moment-to-moment.

Know your traumas, love your traumas,
know your identity and hold it loosely,
know your wounds and care for them.

But most of all,

identify with the free flow of erotic, of life, of God, as it moves through you, moment to moment to moment.

Open and breathe that in. The more that you identify with this free flow, the more your attention is on this free flow, the freer you feel inside yourself.

This doesn't invalidate your wounds and your constriction and your tightness—it honors them.

You are born free. You are born to have sex.

Every ounce of your body is sex. Everything you do, from eating, to moving, to feeling, to grieving, to loving, to taking someone into your body is sex.

You are born as a sexual being, born sexually innocent.

As **Mary Oliver** writes in her poem, *Wild Geese,*
> "You do not have to be good.
> You do not have to walk on your knees for a hundred miles through the desert repenting.
> You only have to let the soft animal of your body love what it loves..."

In other words...

> ***You don't have to deny how deeply erotic you are in order to be good.***

You don't have to deny how deeply erotic you are in order to be good.

As you reclaim your erotic, you reclaim your innate nature.

By reclaiming your erotic, you give life permission to remake you over and over again. Just as the river flows through any barriers, any constrictions, any obligations, that is the power of your sex. When you let your sexuality run through your life, you give your eroticism, your Eros, permission to carve out a path that is uniquely you.

Eros doesn't listen to, "No, I can't. No, I shouldn't." Eros says simply, "I will. I can." At your core, your Eros is unapologetic.

As we get enough of these erotic rivers undammed, unleashed and free flowing, our world becomes saturated, hydrated and nourished from the deep well of the erotic feminine.

> *As you reclaim your erotic, you reclaim your innate nature.*

Invitation: Grab Your Journal

1. How would you describe your sexual experiences so far? What pivotal moments exist in your erotic past?

2. Which of the three levels of sex are you more intrigued to explore right now?

3. On the physical level...

   o Which of the six tips I gave to Amira do you want to try personally? What would that look like?

   o What is your "desire style"—responsive, spontaneous or both? How can this information help you?

   o What turns you on sexually? Create a list of at least ten items.

4. On the emotional level...

   o What emotions have you brought into your sex? What emotions would you be curious to bring into the bedroom next?

   o How honestly do you communicate with your partner(s), both verbally and nonverbally? What can you do to give more honest feedback?

   o How matched are you and your partner's libidos? What could you do about any potential mismatch?

5. On the spiritual level...

   o Have you ever before had sex that felt spiritual or deeply profound? What did it feel like? What did you discover?

   o If you haven't, what do you want it to feel like? How could you open up to more spirituality/God/the divine in your sex?

Exercises for the Physical Level of Sex

The following two exercises are designed to be done with your intimate partner in order to help you both communicate what you like sexually and to better understand each other. These exercises will also help you understand yourself!

Exercise: "Kiss Me Like This"

We often assume that we know what a "great kiss" is. And yet, how often do you talk about it with your partner(s)? Have you ever shared what you like in a kiss?

The below "Kiss Me Like This" exercise is a light, fun way to get to know each other's style.

Here's how to do it:

1. Choose a Person A and a Person B.

2. Person A is the neutral party, who is just there to respond to the kiss in a neutral fashion, following Person B's lead.

3. Person B then approaches and kisses Person A in the exact style they enjoy. Consider where your lips rest, when you use tongue (or not), how fast you approach the other person, how much pressure you use, etc.

4. Person A takes mental notes: "This is how my partner likes to be kissed."

5. Then switch roles and allow Person A to lead the kiss.

6. Debrief by responding to the prompt, "This is what I learned about how you like to be kissed_____" and share what you noticed about y,our partner.

Exercise: "This or That"

This is a flexible exercise you can do in a PG version or a racy version, depending on the body part you choose. It is incredibly helpful for you to understand your own preferences and for your partner to learn your body.

1. Choose a Person A and Person B.

2. Person A is the receiver. They decide the body part they want to do the exercise with (feet, arms, ass, breasts, genitals…choose your own adventure!) and for how long. Person A sets the timer.

3. Assuming Person B is willing, Person B begins to touch that part of Person A's body. Person B will use two different types of touch while asking, "Do you like this….Or that?"

4. Person A feels the two touches and says "this," or "that," indicating their favorite touch.

5. Person B repeats the preferred touch, and adds another type of touch. Types of touch to consider: featherlight strokes, caresses, spanks, scratching with your nails, tickling, poking, hovering your hand over the area, etc. Be creative!

6. When the timer goes off, thank each other, then switch roles. Person B is now the receiver.

7. Debrief with the prompt: "What I learned about myself is_____," and "What I noticed about you is _____."

This exercise is game-changing! James and I did this early on in our relationship, while he went down on me, trying out different strokes and asking "this or that"? It helped me learn more about my pussy and gave him the info he needs to be excellent at that particular activity.

Exercise for the Emotional Level of Sex

The emotional level is a bit more difficult to give a prescriptive exercise for than the physical level, but try this....

1. The next time you'd like to make love with your partner, take a minute to pause. What emotions are you feeling right now? Mad, sad, happy, scared?

2. Let your partner know you're going to practice bringing your emotions into the bedroom, and that you welcome their emotions, as well.

3. Then approach your partner and begin to kiss them with those emotions running through your body. For example ...

    a. If you're angry, maybe you push your partner up against a wall, grab their face, and passionately kiss them.

    b. If you're scared, maybe you shyly approach them, hiding your face behind your hair, and timidly kissing their cheeks.

    c. If you're sad, maybe you move slowly, letting the grief soften your body into their chest.

4. Continue kissing and moving into more erotic activities, feeling the emotion present. Your emotions may change throughout the experience—welcome that! Each new emotion is a new invitation.

5. If you find yourself in your head analyzing your emotions instead of feeling them, pause. Close your eyes, feel your heart, and ask, "What am I feeling now?"

6. After the erotic moment finishes, take turns sharing, "What I loved about that was ____." It can be vulnerable to share our emotions so freely, especially in a sexual context, so make sure to acknowledge yourself and your partner.

Exercise for the Spiritual Level of Sex

Ultimately, you can feel penetrated by the divine during the act of lovemaking, blasted open by the universe.

You can dissolve your separate self and feel ultimate unity with all of life.

You can be utterly and completely transformed by the act of spiritual sex.

Sound like a tall order? It is. Yet it is also 100% possible for you. It just takes practice, skills and a devoted commitment to the erotic.

If you're curious HOW to start bringing spirituality into sex, here are four ways to begin:

1. **Set an intention for the erotic experience** - What do you want to call in or create through this lovemaking? What beneficial impact could your lovemaking have on yourself, your partnership and the world? Consider lighting a candle and saying a prayer to open to space for lovemaking.

2. **See the divine in your partner** - As you look into your partner's eyes, can you see the "God self" inside of him? Can you see his soul, the eternal, wise, and deepest part of him? Touch your partner as if he is sacred and it is an honor to be with him.

3. **Move with breath together** - Breathing deeply and mindfully helps you bring more awareness into your touch. Imagine your breathing is like the rhythm of your lovemaking, the heartbeat of the experience. Match your inhales and exhales so you and your partner are breathing together. Breathing together can help you dissolve a sense of separateness and more fully merge together.

4. **Allow space and stillness** - Spiritual sex is by far the most subtle of the three levels, which means it requires stillness and space to be felt. Kiss passionately or fuck wildly, and then let there be pauses, space to feel into the energy that was just created. Space to sense what wants to happen next between you two, as the surfers waiting for the wave. Only once you feel the impulse to move, begin again.

Spiritual sex is a deep and profound topic upon which I will (hopefully) write another book on someday, but in the meantime, enjoy these books by three of my favorite authors:

- *Urban Tantra* by **Barbara Carrellas**
- *Finding God through Sex* by **David Deida**
- *The Radiance Sutras* by **Lorin Roche**

CHAPTER 14

HAVINGNESS

When we get what we have longed for, we discover a new challenge. Are we the woman who can HAVE this desire? Can we allow ourselves to grow bigger to welcome this desire in?

Receiving our desires is an ego death. It changes who we think we are and requires us to undergo an identity transformation. This process can feel deeply uncomfortable, as we don't recognize ourselves in this new context of our desires. Let me get you caught up on my story...

When I Got It All and Lost My Mind

About eighteen months into living in Bali, I realized—every one of my desires had come to fruition. It was an alarming, amazing moment.

My coaching business, once a tiny struggling idea, was now a full-fledged, six-figure plus enterprise with two sold out retreats under my belt, a full roster of clients and two group programs. I was making twice as much money working for myself as I had as a leadership consultant—something I couldn't have imagined when I'd left my job two years prior.

James and I were happily deepening our commitment. In fact, one Friday night while walking our dogs, he proposed to me. It was so elegant and beautiful—a specially catered dinner waiting, my dream ring, the song I said I wanted at our wedding, the sun setting over the rice paddies. I felt as if I was on the Bachelorette, like this moment was too beautiful to be my own life.

Then we set our sights on buying a house together. I dreamed of a four bedroom, modern home with lots of space to host events, a tropical garden and a pool. Within two weeks, a former student of James contacted him—he had just built that house. As soon as I walked in, I knew—*Yes. This is the place.* Within a month, I was signing the paperwork to buy my first home.

We hosted a big elaborate engagement party with fifty people in our new home. Being surrounded by such a beautiful community felt surreal, because just eighteen months ago, I knew no one and had moved to Bali with zero friends. I was confronted by how quickly I found community and how loved I felt.

All of this goodness was a little too much for my poor ego.

I began picking fights with James, finding flaws and reasons he might not be *the one* for me.
I started seeing our house as a giant burden with an unlimited list of maintenance tasks and dreamed about giving it all away and living in a one bedroom bungalow in the jungle.
I decided I didn't want any more clients and I needed a break at work, so I slowed down my whole enterprise.

At my core, I felt a deep existential crisis—**Who am I now?**

I knew myself as the broke, single, hippie who was desperate to make friends, who had a tiny one bedroom house, no income and was eager to date this charming man.

I didn't know who I was as this homeowner, wife, successful entrepreneur and community leader. It felt surreal, weird, as if this wasn't my life anymore.

That's when I realized, "Oh. I am hitting my havingness."

Hitting Your Havingness

Desire is so utterly confronting because it requires us to expand who we think we are, to grow into someone big enough to hold this larger vision of our life.

Sometimes, we can't yet hold that vision.
Sometimes, we hit a glass ceiling.

As a former teacher of mine called it, sometimes we "hit our havingness."

What does this mean?

Well, we all have a place where we feel safe and secure. This is our comfort zone, or our homeostasis.

Desire is the force that asks us to grow beyond our comfort zone.

When we ask for and receive a desire that is too far outside of our comfort zone, we will (unconsciously) try to sabotage it.

Example: You've dreamt your whole life about a man sweeping you off your feet and taking you on a surprise romantic getaway. When this man arrives with a dozen roses in his hand, all you can think is, "Ew, why did he choose the red roses? So cliché."

Your judgmental voice was a way to block receiving such a beautiful desire. These judgments avoided you feeling vulnerable and touched by the thoughtfulness of his gesture. It was a sign that you have "hit your havingness."

How to Know You've Hit Your Havingness

You can "hit your havingness" when every single thing in your life is going amazingly OR when one particular aspect of your life is blowing your mind.

For example, perhaps you are still struggling professionally, yet you are also in the most intimate, connected relationship of your life. In that case, you may notice signs of "hitting your havingness" specifically in your love life or with this partner though not in your professional life.

In other words, "hitting your havingness" can be situation-specific.

You'll know that you've "hit your havingness" when you find yourself...

- Criticizing other people for tiny flaws
- Criticizing yourself
- Focusing on the negatives in the situation
- Feeling deflated instead of grateful
- Acting nonchalant about a big win
- Quickly spending all the money you just earned
- Overanalyzing the situation
- Obsessive thinking ("What if this goes wrong?")
- Worrying about losing it all

What to do when you see these signs?
First, just notice that you're hitting your havingness. Observe it. Get curious about it.

When you've hit an internal wall of how good you will let your life get, you can't get over that wall with force or self-will. You have to soften into that wall with gentle curiosity.

What You Appreciate, Appreciates

Back to my personal story...so, I hit my havingness and watched myself try to blow it all up. I fought with James, pushed away my friends, slowed down my business and complained about my house. These were all ways I tried to avoid the vulnerability of receiving my desires.

Luckily, with the help of great coaches, I caught myself in the act. I became aware that what I was feeling wasn't actually discontent and dissatisfaction—I had just hit my own glass ceiling of how good I will let my life get.

The antidote to hitting our havingness is gratitude

I began an active gratitude practice. I'd walk around my house and instead of finding flaws or problems to fix, I trained my brain to see what was beautiful in the house. The new little bud on our indoor plants. The way the light streamed into my room in the mornings. The spacious living room where I could host gatherings for my friends.

I took the same approach to my relationship. Instead of finding all the ways that James wasn't *the one*, I renewed my commitment to appreciation. What did I love about him? What am I grateful for in our relationship? Where is he brilliant? I made an effort to tell him at least three things I appreciated about him daily.

I followed suit in my business. First, I let myself take a little break. No new clients, no new programs for a few weeks. It had been a big spring, with my biggest sales in one week ever, and I was feeling a bit burned out. I took a break to celebrate how far I've come in my business. I gave gratitude to my clients, appreciated my favorite moments from the retreat and my group programs and acknowledged the hard work I had put into starting this business.

Celebration was so helpful for me during this time. When I hit my havingness, everything feels like a **problem**, as if something is wrong. Celebrating receiving my desires and giving gratitude flips this script on its head and reminds me, "Oh yes, actually, everything is okay."

Empty what is full, fill what is empty

A teacher of mine once told me the antidote to hitting your havingness is to "empty what is full and fill what is empty." This means noticing when we are "full"—aka we have received our desires, are full of love and abundance and are hitting our havingness.

When this happens, we need to "empty out" by being of service to others, sharing our abundance generously and putting attention on other people. This behavior fills what is "empty" in other people, and gives us relief by having someone else on whom to pay attention.

This axiom has been incredibly important in my life, helping me continue to come back to service when I feel "full." Noticing I had hit my havingness, I realized I needed to empty out and be of service in some way.

Around this time, I started the Bali Women's Fund, an investment fund that gives grants and no-interest loans to Balinese women entrepreneurs. We made a number of investments, some of which are still ongoing. We invested in a group of women recovering from domestic violence to start a garden restaurant for their neighborhood. We gave a loan to our friend's mom so she could build a shop selling produce—which was something for her to feel excited about after she lost her job. We supported traditional weavers in North Bali to reteach their craft after the tourism industry crashed due to Covid-19. We gave grants to an initiative that encourages people to clean up trash from the beaches, and in exchange, gives rice to families in need.

While I hope our grants helped others, I know making the grants definitely helped me. I felt much better having a channel to "empty" and put my attention on others.

Service is immensely helpful when we hit our havingness. So, too, is permission-giving sisterhood, reminding us it is safe to receive it all and shine.

Who Does This B*tch Think She Is?!

I have noticed women may feel uncomfortable receiving their desires because they may worry, "What will other people think?"

I've heard similar fears from my clients, over and over again:

- "If I make a lot of money, will I lose my friends?"
- "If I admit how happy I am with this person, what if he leaves and I look like a fool?"
- "If I publicly share my success, will other women tear me down?"
- "If I make a lot of money, will people judge me as selfish?"
- "If I celebrate myself, will people think I am arrogant or full of myself?"

Can you relate to any of these fears?

I definitely can!

It can be scary—and vulnerable—to admit we are receiving our desires. To admit that we are women who have enough internal power, rightness and magnetism to attract what we want and receive it. This is taboo in a world that prefers the helpless "damsel in distress" to the "sassy, sexy bitch who receives all her desires."

I was sharing this with my friend, Lauren (remember her from Chapter 6?), and she said she uses this question with her friends— "Who does this b*tch think she is?!" to challenge herself and her girlfriends to dream bigger, go bolder and celebrate themselves more.

I love that! Don't you?

"Who does this b*tch think she is?!" feels so freeing. More than anything, women need permission and approval. Permission to acknowledge how powerful we are when we are in our desire, and approval for being women with big appetites for life.

So, my invitation to you: challenge your friends to brag about all the desires they are receiving. Encourage them to celebrate their success with you, and celebrate yours with them. Help each other rise higher through your friendships.

Here's a practical way to do this:

- During your next women's gathering or girlfriend catch up, invite each woman to brag about her life. What is she proud of? What can she celebrate? What desires is she receiving?

- Encourage the woman sharing to take up space fully! Consider using a three-minute timer if that helps your group.

- After she shares, the rest of the group's job is to cheer her on. Celebrate her, encourage her, give her a high-five and in all the ways you can think of, remind her how loved she is in all of her radiant receiving.

- Continue until each woman has a chance to share her brag.

This practice of bragging together and playfully challenging each other with "Who does this b*tch think she is?" encourages women to undo the patriarchal conditioning that tells women to stay small, humble and invisible.

Instead, when we take up space, celebrate ourselves and allow ourselves to feel proud of all we have accomplished and received... we remember how powerful we truly are.

Invitation: Grab Your Journal

1. What can you celebrate yourself for right now? What brags can you share?

2. What desires have you recently received?

3. Do you recognize any of the signs of "hitting your havingness" above?

4. What can you do to "empty what is full" inside yourself? Gratitude, appreciation, service, bragging, etc.?

5. How can you share your joy and gratitude more openly, using the question, "Who does this b*tch think she is?!" as inspiration?

Exercise: 100 Thank You's

All day we are receiving from others—but we are not always aware of it. This exercise is designed to help you notice all the places you are **already** receiving your desires. This opens you up to receive more of your desires and helps you feel more abundant.

Your task is to say, "Thank you," 100 times today. Do you think it is impossible? Think again!

A few examples of moments you may be receiving but not noticing:

- When your partner (or the barista) hands you your coffee
- When your friend invites you to dinner
- When the mail person delivers a package
- When someone intently listens to your story
- When you get a compliment on your outfit
- When your grown children take the time to call you
- When your dog curls up next to you on the sofa
- When your colleague helps you on a project
- Etc.

All of these moments, while tiny, are chances to pause. To notice that you are, in fact, receiving a beautiful act of love. And to express gratitude for it by saying "thank you."

If you run out of moments in the day, consider reflecting on past memories and send a few "thank you" texts or calls to people who have impacted you. You may be surprised at how good it feels.

Can you share 100 thank you's today?

Sustaining

"Impermanence is the goodness of reality. Just as the four seasons are in continual flux, winter changing to spring to summer to autumn; just as day becomes night, light becoming dark becoming light again—in the same way, everything is constantly evolving. Impermanence is the essence of everything...

Somehow in the process of trying to deny that things are always changing, we lose our sense of the sacredness of life.

Pain and pleasure go together; they are inseparable. They can be celebrated. They are ordinary. Birth is painful and delightful. Death is painful and delightful. Everything that ends is also the beginning of something else."

– **Pema Chodron**, When Things Fall Apart

CHAPTER 15

DEATH & THE
IMPERMANENCE OF LOVE

So far, you have **emptied** out regrets and resentments, a bit of "good girl" conditioning and have questioned the cultural stories you inherited. That's the journey of unlearning.

Then, you **reclaimed** your feminine by choosing to turn on, discovering your pussy and pleasure, trusting your desires (shadow and otherwise), listening to your emotions and celebrating your cyclical nature.

In the previous section, you **opened** to love by understanding masculine/feminine dynamics, choosing to trust the masculine, exploring your sexuality and fully receiving your desires.

Finally, we'll look at **sustaining**. How do you live a desire-led, erotically-alive, passionate life...for the long-haul? What is needed to make a lifelong commitment to this way of being?

You may notice that not many people around you live their lives this way. This is far from the norm.

Typically, I see people live their life chasing the next moment and the next, rarely being present, continually doing what they think they're "supposed to do" over what they want to do, and going through the motions of life without much aliveness or feeling.

Is that depressing?
Yes, a bit.

However, if you're reading this book, I trust you are a woman who wants more from life. Who wants to live big, loud and audacious. You want to trust your desires, you want to trust yourself and you want to trust in the power of love.

My hope is that you have glimpsed the possibilities of this kind of living through the stories, questions, and exercises so far in this book. While you may not live in a permanently turned on, alive and vivacious state (and let's be honest—who does?), you've likely surprised yourself with moments of aliveness, brilliant desires and bold requests while you were reading this.

Now, this is where you move from the **possibility** of living a desire-led life to the **probability** of living this way. In other words, this section is about creating the conditions so that trusting yourself and your desires becomes second nature to you.

How?

Sustaining this growth requires two core aspects:

1. A clear *why*—that is the focus of this chapter
2. A great community of women around you to support your evolution—Chapter 16

Let's start with this chapter on death. Are you surprised that we're talking about death?

I'm not surprised if you are surprised. Our culture tends to run at the hint of death. We avoid any mention of it, any hint that we may soon die.

And yet, where does that lead us?

As we run and run from death, we become more and more anxious about living. "We must SEIZE THE DAY!" we urgently insist, as if when we don't SEIZE the day it will slip away from us. We race from moment to moment trying to create some future that doesn't yet exist. We're full of anxiety and insecurity, clinging to "good" moments with desperation while vehemently pushing away "bad" moments.

In short, by trying not to think about death or "bad" things, we are left with a divided soul, one based on fantasy rather than reality.

Let's face it—as my Dad says, "None of us get out of here alive."

You're dying. I'm dying. We're all dying.

Realizing that none of us gets out of here alive can bring a sense of unity. Whether you are rich or poor, healthy or ill, loved or lonely... we're all dying. There is a tragic, connecting beauty in that, isn't there?

Death follows us like our shadow from the very moment we are born. Being born means walking with death, as death is part and parcel of life itself.

By facing death head-on, we can find the courage to live more fully. We stop running from the inescapable and begin to question what really matters to us. Knowing we're already dying gives us the courage to take risks we may not otherwise.

> *"The fear of death follows from the fear of life. One who lives life fully is prepared to die at any moment."*
> —Edward Abbey

A desire-led life may feel scary and uncertain because it requires a million little "ego deaths" along the way before our ultimate physical death. By becoming friends with our physical death, we become more willing to undergo "ego deaths" and take leaps of faith into our desires.

Embracing Duality

We spend much of our lives chasing pleasure, trying to avoid pain.
Chasing love, trying to avoid heartbreak.
Chasing desires, trying to avoid disappointment.
Chasing life, trying to avoid death.

Yet, what if both of these are opposite sides of the same coin?

In Chapter 7, I talked about "picking up both ends of the stick." When we have a desire, we also pick up the fear of not getting that desire, as well as the possibility for rejection, disappointment or pain. Those "darker" aspects are part and parcel of desire—just the other side of the coin. We cannot live a desire-based life without opening ourselves up to pain, disappointment, fear and rejection.

This is true for every "duality" we face in life. If we chase love and try to avoid heartbreak, we will never fully open our hearts to another because we will be too afraid of pain to love fully. If we chase life and try to avoid death, we risk never fully living because we are too afraid to die.

By trying to experience all pleasure and no pain, we divide our soul in two. We push and cajole life to be on our terms and then wonder why we suffer so much depression, anxiety and hostility.

So, what is the antidote?
Embracing both sides of the coin.

Open ourselves to love AND heartbreak.
To desire AND disappointment.
To life AND death.

I'm not afraid of pain

Flash back to my third date with James...I was falling fast in love with him. He, being the more cautious one of the two of us, was feeling nervous about how quickly we were connecting. He said, "I'm afraid I will break your heart."

I said, "Oh, you mean, you're afraid I will one day be curled up on the bathroom floor in the fetal position, sobbing because my heart has been smashed into a million pieces?"

A bit taken aback and uncomfortable, he said, "Yes, exactly. I don't want to do that to you."

I paused, then said quite honestly, "Bring it on. I know myself. I have been heartbroken many times in my life and every time I come back stronger, more resilient. I'm not afraid to have my heart broken. The only thing I am afraid of is never really living and never really loving."

He looked surprised, but nodded. "Yes."

It was a profound moment for me, because I felt the truth in my statement.

Each time my heart breaks, I've discovered the depth of my resilience. I always rise again, usually even stronger than before.

There's a concept called "antifragile," where a substance is neither resistant to pain (strong) nor shatters under pain (fragile), but rather actually **requires** a degree of pain in order to grow stronger. Our muscles are antifragile, for example. When we exercise, the muscle fibers tear slightly and then rebuild stronger. I believe our hearts are also made to be antifragile—that we're meant to love fully and break open, over and over again for our entire lives.

Desire Invites a Thousand Tiny Deaths

Each time I follow my desire, I invite death into my life.

When I began pursuing a personal growth path...I watched many of my old friendships die away as I began forming a new community.

When I quit my consulting job...my identity as a leadership consultant died, and the future career path I'd once envisioned vanished.

When I felt the desire to go to Bali...my life at the retreat center, with the *Orgasmic Meditation* community, died away.

When I started my coaching business...I shut the door on all the other career paths I could have chosen in order to commit to this one. Other options died away.

Every major desire requires us to be willing to "die" to our old way of living. It is an invitation to shed who we were and become who we're next meant to be. Until the next death/desire comes...

> *Every major desire requires us to be willing to "die" to our old way of living. It is an invitation to shed who we were and become who we're next meant to be.*

Everything in our biology and our culture tries to avoid death. "Don't talk about it, don't think about it, just hope for a long life," seems to be the mantra.

Yet if we are to live fully and love fully, we must become intimate with death. Facing death head-on gives us courage to open our hearts more fully, because what do we have to lose?

Death helps me continue to notice and appreciate the beauty of these tiny, ordinary moments, while holding them softly with an open palm.

Every night before James and I fall asleep, I oil his face with this lovely scented face oil. As I caress his cheeks, his forehead and the skin around his eyes, I remember that this face is aging every day. I remember that if I'm lucky, I will live to see this skin wrinkled and paper thin, but even then, one day he will be gone. Being with that reality as I oil his face each night brings an added layer of specialness, devotion and reverence to my touch. I appreciate this little daily ritual more, knowing it is never guaranteed that I'll get to do it again the next day.

Have you heard the old Japanese saying, "Mono No Aware?"

It means *"the ephemeral nature of beauty – the quietly elated, bittersweet feeling of having been witness to the dazzling circus of life – and knowing that none of it can last. It's about being both saddened by and appreciative of transience – and also about the relationship between life and death."* (quote by Fiona Macdonald via BBC.com).

Beautiful, isn't it? That's the feeling to me—bittersweet beauty mixed with deep reverence.

Loving With an Open Palm

Death teaches us to love with an open palm vs. a tight grasp. It invites us to realize how delicate and fragile life is and how powerless we are to control things. Nowhere is this more prevalent than within an intimate relationship.

Death happens a million tiny ways in relationships.
You have a special kiss and then your partner pulls away—that is a death.
You spend a romantic night together and then you have to go to work—that is a death.
You become parents, suddenly focused on a family broader than just the two of you—that is a death.
Relationships are in a constant cycle of death-rebirth-death-rebirth.

We run into trouble when we want to keep everything the same.
Keep the spark alive—always.
Keep the romance hot—always.
Keep our partner the same (and don't grow).

When we're afraid of the "daily deaths" in our relationship, we will try to grip and control. We don't make space for ourselves and our partner to grow and evolve. In trying to avoid these daily deaths, we end up squashing the very thing we hoped to keep—that tender spark of love.

> *Love won't be contained and it certainly won't stay the same.*

323

Love won't be contained and it certainly won't stay the same.

In my relationship with James, we have seen many seasons already in only a few years. Time of hot romance, times of boredom. Times of passionate love, times of apathetic blahness. Times of devotion, times of taking each other for granted. There is constant change in our dynamic.

These changes scared me at first. He was the first man I'd stayed with past the "honeymoon" phase. I was terrified that once that honeymoon phase ended, we may have nothing left. The start of our relationship was so romantic, sexy and powerful... What would happen when the beginning ended?

Well, I've discovered, a new phase begins. For now, something deeper, calmer, more focused on our community and not just ourselves. As we move into marriage, and soon into parenthood, we will have many more relationship "deaths" to navigate together.

Death at Our Wedding

On October 31, 2020, James and I held a commitment ritual weekend with our closest friends. With Coronavirus making travel uncertain, we didn't know when we would be able to bring our families together (who are spread across four continents) for an official wedding. In the meantime, we still wanted to celebrate our commitment to creating a life together.

To this end, we gathered twenty friends to spend a weekend exploring the cycles of death, rebirth and life together. On the first day, we dressed all in black and separated the men from the women. The women meditated on which parts of them were dying while cocooned in the darkness of our bedroom with only candlelight to make out each other's faces.

In flickering candlelight, we shared what is dying in us, honoring the old behaviors, beliefs, habits and identities that are falling away. I shared that in making a lifelong commitment to James, a little of my flighty, self-absorbed nature was dying away. Now I need to consider how my actions would impact him, our relationship, and our future family. I felt a deepening of responsibility and a letting go of frivolousness. I also talked about how marriage represented a closing of doors, letting go of all the other men I could have dated, and instead, wholeheartedly choosing this one man to whom to commit. While of course I was excited to marry James, a part of me needed to grieve the doors I was closing, too. Marriage is a form of death.

The following day, we did a rebirth ritual, followed by our commitment ceremony and then a full moon party. By the time I got to the commitment ceremony, I felt so clear and light. I had grieved and released what was dying in me. I was welcoming in the new parts of me emerging—the wife and someday, the mother. The whole day, I felt soft, grounded in myself and ready to commit wholeheartedly.

When we have major milestones like a wedding, we often only celebrate the "light" aspects of the occasion. We only celebrate the joy of marriage and the hope for the future. Yet in every change, there is also a death, a grieving, a "darker" aspect of letting go of the old to make space for the new. This is when being intimate with death is useful.

> *"Death is very likely the single best invention of life. It is life's change agent. It clears out the old to make space for the new."* – Steve Jobs

How well do you understand that you're going to die? How do you feel about the reality of this?

- Does it feel shocking, scary, unknown?
- Does it feel logical but void of any emotion?
- Does it feel exciting, urgent, creative?

It has been said that each day the Dalai Lama contemplates these statements: "I am going to die. I never know when. What is unfinished?"

As I contemplate those questions, what matters to me comes into sharp focus. In the harsh light of death, I discover that what matters is not my social media likes or the revenue I generate or the tasks I accomplish. What matters to me is loving those around me, being of service to the evolution of humanity, caring for the earth and being present for my life. That is all.

Death Crystallizes What Truly Matters to Us

By meditating on your own death, you may discover a deeper sense of your life's *why*. You may uncover your true priorities and values. You may feel just a little bit more courage to trust yourself and your desires.

Below, I share three of my favorite death meditations inspired from the incredible book, *Wake Up to Your Life* by *Ken McLeod*, which you can listen to for free on Spotify.

I've recorded my own version of the meditations, which you can find for free on my website: **www.megandlambert.com/book**.

I recommend reading each of the meditations, then choosing **one** that most appeals to you right now on which to focus. You can do more meditations later, but start with just one and see how you feel.

Trigger warning: Each of these meditations are intense. You'll be asked to welcome death head on. Take it slowly. Trust yourself to discern what is manageable for you.

Meditation: Death May Come at Any Time

This meditation was particularly useful for me during a difficult transition time, as it made me appreciate each day more. I hope you find it powerful, as well.

_____

Wherever you are right now, look around and see all the ways you could die.

If you're in your kitchen, notice the knives lying around with which you could get stabbed. The electrical shocks that could fry you. The stove that could cover you in burns.

If you're in your living room, realize that a crazed person could barge in and kill you. You could fall and hit your head. You could have a heart attack. Your brain could bleed to death.

As you commute to work, notice the minefield around you. Cars that could crash into you. Trains that could run you over. Passersby who could be terrorists and shoot you. Sick people who could infect you with a novel virus.

Continue using your imagination to see all the ways you could die, allowing yourself to feel the reality of your incredible vulnerability to death.

Let this truth fully sink in.

Be present with any fear, grief, or anger this brings up. Nothing to do, just notice and love any emotions that arise.

You never know when you're going to die.

It can be right now.

It could be just a few minutes from now.

Death can come at any time, and there is nothing you can do about it, except be with that reality.

After I did this meditation daily, I found myself relishing each moment more. I was more present, more appreciative of being alive. I didn't take my health or vitality for granted in the same way.

What do you notice after you do this meditation?

Meditation: Your Body Is Already Dying

This meditation is designed to help you feel the reality of your death in a tangible, embodied way vs. as an abstract intellectual concept.

Our beauty culture is designed to prevent any sign of aging, sickness or impending death. Worldwide, we spend billions of dollars annually avoiding the reality that our body is already dying. This meditation has you confront, face-to-face, the slow decay of your body.

I have found that in confronting this reality, I find more appreciation for my body, my health and my vitality...and lessen my fear of getting older. Ready?

Begin by lying down in a corpse's pose, on your back, with your arms either by your side or resting across your chest.

Imagine your body is buried in the earth.

You've just died.
Your breathing has stopped.
Your heart is no longer beating.
Bit by bit, your organs shut down.
Your mouth is dry as the fluids drain from your body.

Over time, your skin is rotting, peeling away from your flesh.
Worms begin eating away at the muscles and soft tissues
of your body.
Insects and scavengers take what nutrients they can from
your decaying flesh.

Eventually, all that is left are your bones, dry, brittle and
white.
Eventually, even those bones, once so sturdy and solid, turn
to nothing more than dust.
Everything in your body is gone.
You have disappeared.

Take a few breaths to breathe that reality in. Spend at least
five minutes fully integrating the feeling of your body's
decaying.

Then wiggle your fingers and toes, bringing yourself back to
life and back to this moment.

How do you feel? What did you notice?

This meditation gave me a renewed appreciation for my
body. In a way, it is miraculous that I have not yet died. That
the billions of cells inside me continue to hum, multiply and
carry on, full of life. I hope it helps you see the miracle in
your own body, too.

Meditation: The Death Timeline

This meditation brings into sharp focus what truly matters.

I do this meditation whenever I feel as if something is "off" in my life, such as if the way I'm living is not quite aligned with my values. This meditation reveals what needs to be done before I die, and what truly matters to me. After the meditation, I can take an action(s) aligned with my values.

———————————————

Close your eyes and let your body settle.
Feel your breathing move in and out, slowly.

Imagine you are going to die in **six months**.
How would you live those six months?
What would you need to do to feel complete?
What conversations would you have?
What truths would you admit?
What creative projects would you complete?

Now imagine, you will die in **one month**.
How does this shorter timeline impact you?
What is left undone?
How would you spend that final month? With whom?

Imagine you die in **one week**.
What would your final seven days look like?
Who would you see?
What would you create or complete?

Imagine you die **tomorrow**.
How do you spend your final hours?
What final conversations do you have?
What's unsaid?
What tasks do you finish?

Finally, imagine you die **right now**. How do you feel dying? Peaceful? Scared? Regretful? Anxious? Serene?

_____

After you complete this meditation, take a minute to journal on what you realized. Consider:

- What themes emerged for you?
- What was truly important to you, knowing death was near?
- What desires became more urgent?
- How can you use this knowledge to better align your days?

Invitation: Grab Your Journal

1. How do you feel about death right now? Write down any emotions or feelings without judgment. Welcome them.

2. What does contemplating death bring up in you? Any new perspectives, desires or values?

3. What were the meditations like for you? Which of the three did you feel intuitively drawn to most? Why do you think that is?

4. What desires feel most urgent now, considering you never know when you will die?

5. What part of you is dying right now? What part of you is being reborn?

6. Think of your next milestone (new career, move, new relationship, etc.). Can you imagine incorporating death into it as a way to honor what is dying in you? What would that look like?

CHAPTER 16

IGNITED SISTERHOOD

In the previous chapter, we explored how befriending death can give us courage to follow our big, life-changing desires. Following our big desires also requires supportive women friendships. This chapter is devoted to sisterhood and the immensely supportive power of women friendships.

Some women feel great around sisterhood, have a strong network of support and are proud of their tight network. Unfortunately, many women I know struggle with their female friendships.

We've learned a few quite dysfunctional scripts on how to relate with other women through the media and culture. I grew up with movies including Mean Girls, Bring It On and Stick It, which emphasized competition, hierarchy and gossip among women.

Women-to-women relationships don't have to be that way. We can learn to lift each other up, forgive hurts and create a truly supportive network of women. This chapter will explore how.

My Shaky Foundation of Sisterhood

Growing up, I was a social "floater" who moved between groups, befriending lots of girls but not getting too close to any one person.

My early years with girlfriends were a bit rocky. I felt most comfortable "leading" my group of friends, which meant I was quite bossy and told everyone what to do. In high school, I had a core group of friends whom I enjoyed...until I found out they gossiped about me behind my back.

In college, my friendship strategy was to diversify, so I made lots of friends in many different social circles. I didn't let any one woman get too close to my heart, as I was scared of depending on any woman. The truth was, I didn't trust women.

History repeated itself when I felt my friend group in the sorority slowly begin to exclude me.

In college, I had a group of sorority sisters who were my closest friends. They hung out together daily, while I was often busy with my leadership positions, studying and other obligations. One Thursday night, however, I was ready to go out with them!

My friends arrived all dressed up at the sorority house. I was so excited! I asked them to wait just one minute while I grabbed my bag from upstairs so I could join them for that evening's fraternity party. When I came downstairs, they were gone. They'd left for the party without me.

I snuck back to my bedroom and cried. I had been feeling slowly excluded and vaguely unwanted by this group for months. Them leaving for the party without me made it feel even more real. I was heartbroken.

Unfortunately, I didn't have the tools to repair the relationships at that point in my life, so I never told them how much that moment hurt, nor did I get to understand why they'd excluded me.

This pattern—of getting close to a group of women and then being excluded from them—has been repeated at several different points in my life. It's painful, and it has made me want to avoid sisterhood.

In this slow exclusion, I realized how desperately I wanted to belong and how painful it was to be left out. That insight has helped me cultivate compassion for others who may feel left out, as well.

The truth is, I wasn't just the victim of betrayal—I also wasn't a great friend myself.

I remember attending a women's group in the *Orgasmic Meditation* community, where we were talking about sisterhood. I said, "Oh I love sisterhood. It's so important to me." The leader turned to me and said, "No, you don't like sisterhood, Megan. You like being better than other women." *Ouch.*

At the time, I thought this comment was unjustified and mean. But slowly I began to see—she was right. I was nervous around other women and I didn't trust them, so my protective strategy was to try to be better than them (see Chapter 9 on "Shame"). I tried to dominate my friend groups so I felt safer, more in control and less likely to be excluded.

That strategy doesn't work. Whether I felt less than or better than other women, I still felt deprived of the nourishment of real friend-ships based on equality.

Can you relate?

Many women I talk to have similar "horror stories" of hurts that have happened in their sisterhood. Without the tools we're learning in this book around expressing our emotions and desires, understanding our protective strategies, forgiving others and ourselves, etc., we are left ill-equipped to navigate the dynamic, complex world of women-to-women relationships.

Luckily, it does get better. As I examined my relationships with women, I realized the way I treated other women was a direct reflection of how I treated my own feminine. When I trusted my feminine, I more easily trusted women.

I began taking an honest inventory of how I was showing up for women.

- No more gossiping—I'd change the subject if someone else brought up gossip.

- No more trying to control and lead—I'd trust where the group wanted to go.
- No more radical self-reliance—I'd ask for help, instead.

I wasn't perfect, but these were my commitments. I wanted to learn to be a good friend, to be a good sister to other women. It was a humbling, sometimes painful journey, but now I am so proud of and nourished by my female relationships. More on that soon.

Why Sisterhood Is Challenging

How are your relationships with other women? Easy, difficult, rewarding, painful?

Let's do an honest reflection.
Have you ever...

- Gossiped about another woman?
- Betrayed another woman's trust? Shared one of her secrets?
- Stolen another woman's intimate partner? Or flirted with that person?
- Dismissed another woman's emotions?
- Excluded another woman from the group?
- Made fun of another woman?
- Felt superior to another woman?
- Avoided another woman because you felt inferior to her?
- Tried to dominate other women?

These behaviors are all too common. Many of us have been hurt by female friendships—and we have hurt other women. If we're honest with ourselves, we may not have been exactly perfect in our friendships—and that is okay. Learning to be a good friend to other women can take time, honesty, self-responsibility and willingness.

Frankly, I've been bitchy and judgmental in my friendships, as the below story illustrates.

"You're So Self-Absorbed!"

I stood in the bathroom fuming with my *FemRising* retreat guest teacher, Aimee. We had just finished co-leading a coaching circle together.

"Aimee, I'm judging you," I told her bluntly.
"I know," she replied. "I can feel it. Do you want to share what you're thinking?"

First, you need to know that Aimee has done work on herself the same way I have done work. I don't recommend dumping out all your judgments on most people, but in this case, I knew she could handle it.

"Yes. The voices in my head are saying that you are self-absorbed, arrogant, loud and attention-seeking. That you make the situation all about you and you take up all the space. There is no space left for me to speak. You share all your stories all the time and end-lessly talk about yourself," I ranted.

Phew. It felt good to get those mean voices out of my head.
I knew my judgments revealed more about me than they did about her. But still, those voices were loud!

She laughed and teased me. "Meg, do you want to take up more space and talk about yourself? Do you want more attention?"

I blushed. *Yes, I did.*

I have always been reluctant to ask for attention, and even more so in this context where I was holding a group of participants. Consciously, I wanted to be of service, to give attention to the participants, to focus on their needs and their experiences. But clearly, a shadow part of me was demanding more attention, because here I was judging Aimee for that behavior.

I was embarrassed to admit that I craved more attention. It felt a little shameful.

Yet once I admitted and owned my desire to take up more space, I realized how helpful this insight could be for the group. I shared more personal stories in my teaching, more confidently led the group and I asked for the exact support I needed from my co-facilitators.

Now, of course, my judgments may have revealed insights for Aimee on her behavior, too. But my practice is to keep the attention on my own growth, and so in this moment I allowed my judgments to reveal my own shadow side rather than make this about her and her growth.

Later in the retreat, I jokingly called my shadow side "Mega-B"—the part of me that is like Cardi-B, attention seeking, loud, hungry for fame, self-absorbed and unapologetic. She lives in me because I judge her in others.

For better or worse, what we observe in others tells a lot about our own inner world.

We see ourselves in other women. Our brilliance and our flaws, our fears and our desires. Understanding that our judgments of other women often reveal our inner world allows us to approach friendships with an unprecedented level of self-responsibility.

No longer blaming or shaming her, we can understand who we are better through the realm of friendship. This makes us more accepting of ourselves and of other women. Through this process, we become more available for deep, intimate sisterhood.

Ready to give this process a try for yourself?

She Is Your Mirror.

This process is incredibly insightful, yet it will require your complete honesty and willingness. We're going into taboo territory here.

Whom do you judge?

First question: Whom are you judging?

Be completely honest with yourself about the type of women you judge. Give yourself permission to admit your "bitchy," judgmental side.

For example, as illustrated in the story above with Aimee, I judge loud, self-centered women who talk all about themselves and are endlessly bragging about how great they are. I judge them as narcissistic, self absorbed, selfish and attention-seeking.

Your turn—whom do you judge?

Next question, what are three of the qualities that you see in the women you judge?

No need to play nice here—just the exact words your inner judgy bitch uses.

Your words might be:

- Self-centered
- Fake
- Phony
- Rude
- Vain
- Manipulative
- Attention-seeking
- Narcissistic
- Etc.

Claiming these qualities

This is where the process gets really interesting.

Can you claim these qualities for yourself?

Try saying this out loud. "She is _____[insert the three adjectives from above]...just like me."

For example:
"She is bitchy, vain and entitled...just like me."
"She is narcissistic and self absorbed...just like me."

How does that feel to say out loud?

The truth is that if we are to be whole, we must hold within us ALL of these traits. Whatever traits we don't feel safe enough to admit and own lies in our shadow.

We reveal what's in our shadow by what traits we judge in other people

Imagine a newborn baby. That baby holds every trait of humanity inside of her. The baby is light, dark, good, bad, sweet, angry, etc. As the baby grows up, she learns that some traits are "good" to be, while other traits are "bad." She discovers that some traits get her loved, and others cause her to be rejected. This is the process of social conditioning.

As a result, the baby begins to contort herself and try to become who she thinks she should be. She will reject parts of herself in order to belong and be loved. As she gets older, she will judge anyone who demonstrates the traits she has rejected inside herself.

Why does this matter? Well, in order to feel whole and accept ourselves completely, we have to be willing to embrace and own all of these parts of us.

Not only does this process help us to accept ourselves completely, it also makes us more available for connection with other people. Over time, we will judge people less and accept them more.

If you spot it, you've got it

As any little kid on the playground will tell you, "If you spot it, you got it," or, "It takes one to know one." What does this mean? It means that anything you see in someone else reflects something inside of you.

Kaitlin gets jealous

At my first *FemRising* retreat, my good friend Kaitlin joined us at the last minute after her husband gifted her the retreat. She was touched and delighted to be there, but also...extremely jealous.

In one of the coaching circles, she told me, "Megan, I'm so jealous of you."

I asked, "Oh yeah? Tell me more."

She continued, "You are running a retreat—I want to do that! I've been studying this content as long as you have, so I could do this, too. I'm jealous that you've already put a retreat together. I'm happy to be here, but I can't stop feeling this bitter envy."

I cheered. "Yes!! I love your envy. Do you know why?"

"No," she replied.

"I love your envy because it points back to your desire—to run a retreat. What you see in me, you also see in yourself, right? Now the only difference is what you tell yourself about that desire. You can contract around the desire, think it is impossible and become envious. Or you can open, expand, say, 'I can have that too,' and get inspired. The choice is yours."

She nodded. Over the week-long retreat, she continued to open to the envy she felt and realized she could learn about herself and her desire by studying her envy.

For example, she saw my two dogs, felt envious, and realized she wanted a dog herself. A few months later, she got a dog she loves. She was envious of me traveling with James, and so got inspired to take a belated honeymoon with her partner.

In all of this, her envy wasn't a *problem*—it was a neon sign pointing back to her own desire. By spotting her desire in another woman, she discovered it for herself.

For better or worse, we see ourselves in other women.
We see our shadow by judging her.
We see our desire by envying her.
We can also see our own brilliance by loving her.

What's Possible in Ignited Sisterhood?

Your connections with other women can become your safety net, empowering you to take bigger risks. Sisterhood can provide you security and comfort so you can be brave in your love life. Sisterhood can inspire you to dream bigger, dive deeper and love yourself more.

While deep connections with other women can be terrifying and painful, they can also be profoundly beautiful, helping you become the woman you are meant to be.

Will you let yourself be supported? Held? Loved? Celebrated?
Will you commit to supporting, holding, loving and celebrating other women?
Will you be generous with your time, attention and vulnerability to cultivate these bonds?

Our women-to-women relationships have the power to lift us up, inspire us, turn us on and transform us.

Why is SISTERHOOD, rather than friendship with any gender, so important?

There is a unique experience of being met by other women, particularly around events and experiences to which only other women can relate—menstruation, pregnancy, childbirth and menopause, among many others.

These are powerful experiences of womanhood, and when we gather to share our personal stories, healing happens. We no longer feel alone. We can feel met, understood, seen.

When we neglect our women friendships and instead rely on a partner for all our intimacy needs or focus only on work, then we will feel something is missing. A vital part of being a female.

For hundreds of thousands of years, the women of the tribe would gather to support each other. They'd pick berries together as they bounced their little ones on their hips. They'd teach each other how to manage their monthly cycles and bleeds. They'd support pregnant mamas and be there after birth to nourish her and the baby. They'd share stories of love and loss, the ups and downs of being a woman.

Particularly in times of transition and milestones, we need other women. Starting our cycle. Having sex for the first time. Leaving home. Falling in love. Committing to marriage. Getting pregnant. Giving birth. Starting a business.

These are moments when we are tender, raw, uncertain. We don't yet know how to be in these new milestones. That's where support from other women is especially critical. To hold our hand, to guide us, to hug us, to cheer us on.

Does an ancient part of you remember this way of being with other women? Do you long for it?

Turn on spreads woman to woman

Take a minute and notice how you're impacted when a woman close to you expresses her desire and receives it. I don't know about you, but I tend to feel more alive, electric and full of possibilities. Seeing her have her desire reminds me what is possible. There's something powerful about women supporting each other in that way, as we have the unique ability to turn each other on with our desire.

In this way, turn on spreads woman to woman, creating a bonfire that can light the entire world on fire. When I first started personal growth work, my *why* was to become so lit up that women around me couldn't help but feel more alive, passionate and turned on just by being near me.

Will you commit to being a woman who has an impact like that? A woman who lives so turned on and so passionately that her life becomes an inspiration to other women? A woman who lets herself be inspired by other women, too?

This kind of sisterhood requires that you show up fully—for yourself and for the women you befriend. It requires that you are there when your sisters need you and that you ask for the support you need. It also requires that you don't tolerate your sister's BS excuses for living a life she doesn't love and instead encourage her to trust her desires more fully. Only through that kind of intense backing is real, deep sisterhood possible.

For most of my life, I have craved that type of deep sisterhood but have struggled to find it. Luckily, that's changing.

Women's Rebirth Ritual

Can I admit a secret fear I've held all my life?

It sounds silly and superficial, but I've had the fear that I won't have the right bridesmaids at my wedding. I was afraid that either no one would show up or it wouldn't be right in some way.

Over the past decade, I've lived all over the world and changed so much that I don't have a core lifelong group of girlfriends. I have experienced so much shame around that. I was afraid when I got married that I'd feel like a loser without a core group of lifelong girlfriends.

When I moved to Bali, I began cultivating my friend group consciously and deliberately. I drew up all my courage to ask new women out for coffee, to send vulnerable messages and to keep my attention on how my friends were doing. I was ready to commit to deep sisterhood.

This effort had an impact. During my commitment ritual with James (the same one I mentioned in the previous chapter), I felt supported by my community of women. As you know, each day was designed around a theme—death, rebirth, celebration.

The morning of the commitment ritual, my friends Mesi and Persia planned a rebirth ritual for me. We created a flower mandala and did a womb meditation followed by sensual dance. (Very hippie, I know!) My favorite part, though, was when the women gave me blessings, sharing with me the impact my love has had on them. Woman after woman shared from the heart, telling me moments when I'd inspired them, touched them, loved them. I was in tears the whole time. We all were.

Looking around at the women in the circle, I felt as if I belonged. I felt I was wanted, needed, important. That I mattered. I had never felt so held by sisterhood.

After the blessings, the women covered me in flowers, massaged me and whispered sweet words into my ears. I breathed and let all that love in. Their love and support felt like spiritual nourishment to me, centering me and giving me the courage to make a lifelong commitment to James.

Cultivating these deep bonds of sisterhood has taken real effort, commitment, and energy on my part—yet it is so, so worth it.

Are you ready to build deep, intimate sisterhood, or deepen the friendships you already have? The following exercises will help you do just that.

Exercise: Mark a Milestone with Feminine Ritual

Background

As mentioned, sisterhood is especially important during the milestone moments of being a woman. In these transitions, we are vulnerable, tender and maybe scared, and having the support of other women can make all the difference.

Reflect on the women in your life. Who is approaching a milestone right now?

Consider who may be:

- Starting their menstrual cycle
- Leaving home
- Having sex for the first time
- Falling in love
- Committing to marriage
- Getting pregnant
- Giving birth
- Starting a business
- Going through menopause
- Grown children leaving the home (new empty nester)
- Retiring from work

Does any milestone come to mind?

If not, you can always honor birthdays as a marker of time.

Instructions

1. Ask the woman approaching the milestone if she'd like a sisterhood ritual supporting her transition. If yes, continue on.

2. Choose a date. For added feminine juiciness, consider the moon cycles and select a full moon or a new moon for this ritual.

3. Invite five to ten women to gather on the selected date. This can be at your house, in a park if the weather is nice, at a restaurant, or even virtually on a video chat, if needed. The most important part is that the women attending are fully committed to being present to support the woman moving through a milestone.

4. Decorate the space. Flowers, candles or crystals can help create the feeling of a sacred space for the ritual. It can be simple, but the act of decorating is symbolic. It shows we are moving from "everyday life" to ritual space, a time for something special.

5. When the women arrive, feel free to chit chat for a bit (maybe thirty minutes) to let people settle and then begin the ritual. If done virtually, it's best to move right into the ritual.

6. Seat everyone in a circle, including the woman being supported.

7. If you'd like, you can open the circle with singing, a poem, a prayer, or any other way you'd like to mark the beginning of the ritual.

8. Invite the woman being supported to share for five minutes or so, without interruption, about her transition. How is she feeling? What part of her is dying? What part of her is being born at this moment? What support does she need?

9. After that, invite each woman supporting to give a blessing to the woman in transition. It could be a

prayer, a wish for her or something she loves about the woman.

    a. Note: This is **not** a time for advice-giving. Trust that the woman in transition will figure out what she needs to know. This is a time for LOVE giving. Encouragement, kind words and blessings are welcome.

10. Once every woman has spoken, close the circle. This could be with a song, poem, prayer, showering the woman with flower petals, or any other way that feels good to you.

11. Complete! Celebrate yourself for showing up for the women in your life. Well done—you just created an experience that the woman in transition may remember her entire life.

Exercise: Ask for Support

Background

I often feel awkward or shy when asking for support. I don't know what I even need help with! Then I have to be willing to be vulnerable and risk rejection? What if I am a burden? Ugh, no thanks.

Can you relate?

Many of the strong, powerful women I know struggle to ask for and receive support from girlfriends.

And yet...how do you feel when a good friend shares a struggle and asks for your support? I feel touched that she let me into her heart and honored that I get to help her.

A few months ago, my friend Stephanie reached out to me saying, "Meg, I just finished a tough therapy session and I feel like I need a girlfriend heart-to-heart. Can I come over?"

"Of course!" I replied. A few hours later, we were cuddled on my bed, drinking my homemade "Christmas" tea (a mix of cinnamon, cloves, nutmeg, and honey), sharing what's on our hearts. It was so cozy, connecting and loving. I felt much closer to her after that and touched that she'd reached out. She admitted she was scared to ask for support because she didn't want to be a burden to me, but decided to lean in and ask anyway. I'm so glad she did.

The following exercise will help you ask for support, just like Stephanie did.

Instructions

1. Consider a place that feels tender in your life right now. Examples:

   a. Struggles in your love life?

   a. Hard to believe in yourself professionally?

   b. Wanting to start a new creative project but feel afraid?

2. What kind of support would feel great in that spot? Be as specific as possible. Examples:

   a. A hug or physical touch?

   b. Comforting words to reassure you?

   c. Straightforward feedback?

   d. An honest reflection?

   e. Wise advice?

3. Then, think of your friends. Who feels available and trustworthy to you? Use your intuition here to discern the right person. If you're not sure, just ask

someone. Their response gives you good information on their future availability.

4. Send that person a message or call them. Share what you're struggling with and ask for the exact support you want. Example:

   a. "I'm struggling with _____. I could use your support. Would you ____?"

5. See what happens! Receive the support if it is there.

6. Remember, if the friend says no or is unavailable to support you, that's okay. We aren't always 100% available for each other for whatever reason. Hearing a "no" doesn't mean your request was wrong in any way. You just get to find another friend to ask!

7. Notice how it feels to ask for the support, and then if you do, how it feels to receive that support. Do you feel closer? More intimate?

Invitation: Grab Your Journal

1. On a scale of 1-10, how satisfied and fulfilled do you feel with your female friendships right now? Do you feel loved, supported and met?

2. What would a "10" (highest satisfaction) in your female friendships look and feel like? Be specific and tangible here.

3. What holds you back from creating "10" level sister-hood in your life? What fears, beliefs, behaviors or old habits get in your way?

4. What change can you commit toward your desired level of sisterhood?

Conclusion

YOU ARE A REVOLUTION

If you've made it this far in Eros, if you've done the exercises and/or meditations, if you've discovered something new about yourself...

Celebrate yourself! Give yourself a pat on the back, a mental high-five or a celebratory shimmy shake.

You are an Erotic Rebel, a woman working toward freedom for herself and others, a woman who lets her desire (rather than her fear) lead, a woman who is bravely opening her heart to the world.

You—and women like you—are changing the world. Can you feel it?

We're both part of a bigger revolution happening, a seismic shift in the way the world views the feminine as equally important and just as needed as the masculine.

As we reclaim our desires, we invite other women to give themselves permission to do the same.
As we clear our sexual shame and become freer in our bodies, we inspire other women that this is possible.
As we courageously open our hearts and trust in love, we light the way for other women to follow.
As we honor our own feminine, we learn reverence for the bigger feminine—Mother Earth.

This is a profound journey. I want you to know that the work you're doing is for you, yes, and it is so much bigger than you or me. We are revolutionaries. The revolution is now, here, in your body, in your being.

I want you to know that you matter deeply. That other women are watching you. That your daughters, nieces, granddaughters, students and friends are all observing how you show up in the world. They are understanding at a deep level what is possible for them, as well.

May you be the light that says, "Yes. I am free. I am whole. I am allowed to want, to desire, to feel pleasure, to love wholeheartedly, to create a life I want...I am a woman and I fucking love it."

THANK YOU

I am so grateful to the people who came before me and who taught me how to live more fully.

First, a big thank you to my mentors and teachers. I feel so much gratitude for Nicole Daedone, Regena Thomashauer, Reverend Joanne Coleman, Carolyn Elliott, Byron Katie, Pema Chodron, Maya Angelou, and so many more teachers who have helped me learn what it means to be a woman in these modern times. My life is forever changed because of your work.

I also want to thank you, the reader. This book represents my heart and soul of what I've learned so far in my journey to connecting with Eros. Thank you for making space for me to express my vulnerability and for the gift of your time and attention. I know there are many books you could be reading right now, and I am honored you chose mine. Thank you.

Thank you to my parents, who have been so supportive of me through this journey, even when it didn't make sense to them. It can be challenging to have daughter who carves her own path, especially one based on the erotic, and yet, I have felt supported the whole time by my family. Thank you for your unconditional love and care.

Massive gratitude to my life partner, James. Every step of the way, he encouraged me, cheered me on and gave me honest feedback. He's an integral part of my journey, of this book, and of the woman I am becoming.

Lastly, I am grateful for my daughter-to-be. When I began this book, I was newly married, not yet ready for family. As the work progressed, so did I, and I became ready for motherhood. Now, in finishing the book, I am also finishing my first pregnancy—with a baby girl. Writing a book on the feminine as I grow a baby girl in my womb feels more than a little symbolic. Thank you, baby girl, for choosing me to be your mother.

BOOKS TO ENJOY

I always love new book recommendations so thought you might, as well! Below is a list of my favorites. I'm constantly updating this list as I find new inspiring books, so be sure to check out the latest version of this list on my website: **www.megandlambert.com/book**.

For feminine empowerment...
Pussy: A Reclamation by Regena Thomashauer
The Wild Woman's Way by Michaela Boehm
Rise Sister Rise by Rebecca Campbell
Women Who Run with Wolves by Clarissa Pinkola Estés
Untamed by Glennon Doyle

For your sex life...
The Ethical Slut by Dossie Easton and Janet Hardy
Women's Anatomy of Arousal by Sheri Winston
The Art of Sexual Magic by Margo Anand
Existential Kink by Carolyn Elliot
Slow Sex by Nicole Daedone
Finding God through Sex by David Deida
Urban Tantra: Sacred Sex for the 21st Century by Barbara Carrellas

For knowing your cycles...
The Red Tent by Anita Diamant
Moon Time by Lucy H. Pearce
The Fifth Vital Sign by Lisa Hendrickson-Jack

For navigating partnership...
Celebrating Partnership by Alison A. Armstrong
The Amazing Development of Men by Alison A. Armstrong
Understanding Women by Alison A. Armstrong
The Queen's Code by Alison A. Armstrong
I Need Your Love, Is that True? by Byron Katie
The Awakened Woman's Guide to Everlasting Love by Londin Angel Winters

For living creatively...
The Big Leap by Gay Hendricks
Steering by Starlight by Martha Beck
Big Magic by Elizabeth Gilbert
Do Less by Kate Northrup
Girl, Stop Apologizing by Rachel Hollis
The Power of Vulnerability by Brené Brown

REFERENCES & SOURCES CONSULTED

American Society for Aesthetic Plastic Surgery. "Cosmetic (Aesthetics) Surgery National Data Bank Statistics" ASPS. 2018. https://www.surgery.org/sites/default/files/ASAPS-Stats2018_0.pdf.

Angelou, Maya.1984. *I Know Why The Caged Bird Sings*. London: Virago Press.

Atalanta, Hilde (@the.vulva.gallery @hildeatalanta) "This week is all about pubic hair!" Instagram, February 12, 2021. https://www.instagram.com/p/CLMnUGGFDUY/?utm_source=ig_web_copy_link.

Brown, Brené. "Listening to Shame" TED. March 16, 2021. Long Beach, California. 20:38. https://youtu.be/psN1DORYYV0

Chodron, Pema. 1997. *When Things Fall Apart*. Boston, MA: Shambhala Publications Inc.

Elliott, Carolyn. 2020. *Existential Kink*. Newburyport, MA: Weiser Books.

Jung, Carl. 1958. *The Undiscovered Self*. London: Routledge.

Katie, Byron. "The Work of Byron Katie" Byron Katie International. May 27, 2021. https://thework.com/

Katie, Byron. 2005. *I Need Your Love—Is That True?* London: Rider.

Multidisciplinary Association for Psychedelic Studies. "FDA Agrees to Expanded Access Program for MDMA-Assisted Therapy for PTSD" MAPS. January 17, 2020.
https://maps.org/news/media/8008-press-release-f da-agrees-to-expanded-access-program-for-mdma-assisted-psychotherapy-for-ptsd

Rupani, OM. 2017. *Prerequisites to Ecstasy*.

Thomashauer, Regena. 2016. *Pussy: A Reclamation.* London: Hay House UK.

UNWomen. "Facts and figures: Ending violence against women" UNWomen.org. March, 2021. https://www.unwomen.org/en/ what-we-do/ending-violence-against-women/facts-and-figures

Winston, Sheri. 2010. *Women's Anatomy of Arousal*. Kingston, NY: Mango Garden Press.